SECRETS OF MINOS

Sir Arthur Evans' Discoveries at Crete

ALAN HONOUR

SECRETS

OF MINOS

SIR ARTHUR EVANS' DISCOVERIES AT CRETE

Foreword by Dr. John H. Young, Vickers Associate Professor
of Archaeology, The Johns Hopkins University

illustrated with photographs
and line drawings

McGRAW-HILL BOOK COMPANY
New York • Toronto • London • Sydney

Also by Alan Honour

CAVE OF RICHES: The Story of the Dead Sea Scrolls
TEN MILES HIGH, TWO MILES DEEP: The Adventures of the Piccards
TREASURES UNDER THE SAND: Woolley's Finds at Ur

Library of Congress Catalog Card Number: 60-15285

2 3 4 5 6 7 8 VBVB 7 5 4 3 2 1 0 6 9 8

for

Elinor, Meado, and Debbie Zaki

with love

Acknowledgments

The author wishes to express his deep gratitude to Miss Joan Evans for permission to quote from her book on the Evans family, TIME AND CHANGE (Longmans, Green, & Co., Ltd., London, 1943), and for supplying family photographs. Miss Evans' cooperation was invaluable.

Grateful acknowledgment is due the Agathon Press, Inc., N.Y., for permission to reprint the photographs of the Minoan bronze figurine from Crete, and the Shrine of the Double Axes from THE PALACE OF MINOS AT KNOSSOS by Sir Arthur Evans.

Grateful acknowledgments are due, also, to Mr. Dimos Theodossiades and Mr. Theofilos Chalkiadakis of Iraklion, Crete, for providing me with up-to-date, original photographs of the Palace of Minos at Knossos.

Special thanks to Mrs. Frances Makarai and Mrs. Barbara Blackman of the State Library, Indianapolis, Indiana, and to Mrs. Harriet Bard, Mrs. Hazel Thorne, and the staff of Morrisson Reeves Public Library, Richmond, Indiana, all of whom made possible my study of the books written by Sir Arthur Evans.

The author wishes to give sincere thanks to Mrs. A.J. Honour, of Oxford, England, for her alert research.

Contents

Foreword

I am very glad that Alan Honour has now given our young readers an account of the life and work of Sir Arthur Evans. Sir Arthur was one of the few men who have almost singlehandedly uncovered a whole civilization whose very existence was hitherto unsuspected. He shared the extraordinary vision of Heinrich Schliemann in his confidence that such a civilization must exist, and in a way perhaps surpassed Schliemann's achievement. Schliemann (the subject, by the way, of another book by Mr. Honour), by proving the existence of a Bronze Age culture in Greece, and by showing that much of Greek "mythology" was in fact a record of this culture, well deserves the admiration we all bestow upon him. Yet his discoveries at Troy concerned a city only, and we know today that the inhabitants of his Mycenae and Tiryns were early Greeks. Sir Arthur, on the other hand, discovered a whole new people who had created a civilization uniquely their own, and the problems of their unknown language and their relationships to other known ancient peoples are as baffling today as they were in 1900 when the first hints of their civilization were uncovered. And whatever their origins, the influence of these people on the early Greeks was profound; this alone assures them their important place in history.

Mr. Honour has gone through a great deal of original material to put together his story, and much of it is fresh even to those who thought they already knew it well.

Since this book was written, there has been an attack in the popular press claiming that Sir Arthur distorted certain information contained in a notebook kept while Knossos was being excavated. Mr. Honour has included some final paragraphs in answer to these charges, but the contemptible manner in which they were pressed deserves no answer. That a man who suddenly discovers a lost world will make mistakes in interpreting details is evident to all; they must remember that he alone has the heavy responsibility of measuring the relative importance of each new potsherd and each emerging, and sometimes infinitesimal, layer of soil. Since he will be censured for even the most trivial errors, he should in turn be praised in accordance with all that he has done that is right. Our knowledge of the completely charming new world of Minoan Crete, with its magnificent palaces, its lovely country houses, its gay paintings, all its freedom and light and spontaneous love of nature—all this, then, is the proper testimonial to Sir Arthur Evans.

John H. Young, Ph.D.
Vickers Associate Professor of Archaeology
The Johns Hopkins University

SECRETS OF MINOS

Sir Arthur Evans' Discoveries at Crete

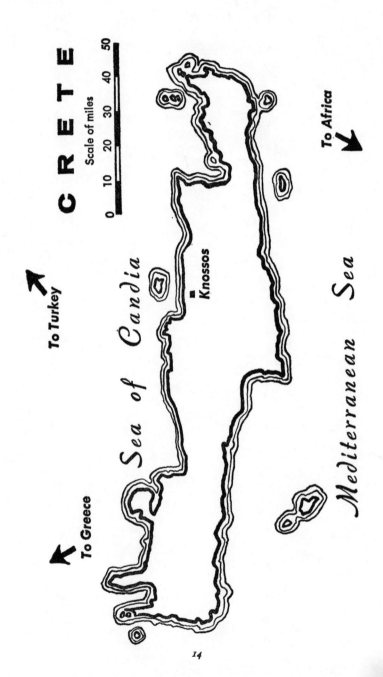

CRETE

Scale of miles

0   10   20   30   40   50

To Greece

To Turkey

Sea of Candia

Knossos

Mediterranean Sea

To Africa

14

ONE

The Fool and His Stick

EARLY in the year 1900, peasants on the Greek island of Crete were amused, their curiosity aroused by a strange little figure who was poking about their countryside. It was not the first time this stranger had been in Crete. He had made several previous visits, but this time he seemed to have a purpose.

Obviously, the stranger was a man of importance, since he had easy access to high-placed men in the capital town of Candia, but he certainly didn't look it! This odd-looking man, with head slightly bent at an unusual angle, was quiet and reserved. He wandered about wearing a battered felt hat upon his head, a shabby raincoat draped from his shoulders.

"What would you expect?" one native said to another. "He's English. All the English are mad, as everybody knows!"

Yet Arthur Evans, the Englishman, was well liked, too.
His twinkling eyes were usually smiling, and most of the
peasants felt kindly and protective toward this unusual
man.   They did not mind the big stick he carried aslant
his shoulder.   For all his oddity, this man was clearly
from the nobility, and he was obviously searching for
something on their island.   Also, many of them knew of
the great poet, Lord Byron, the English nobleman who
had devoted his life and much of his own money in the
fight for Greek freedom, because of his passionate love
for the ancient civilization of the Greeks, motherland
of Crete.   The love the Greeks bore for Byron extended
to many visiting Englishmen.

Crete, with its 656 miles of rugged coastline, was not
too thickly populated.   The harbor at Candia (modern
Iraklion) with limited facilities, had little value for shipping.   The island was 35 miles at its widest point, nar-
rowing to 7 or 8 miles, and a mere 170 miles long.
There was no industry, but the rocky landscape was
thickly dotted with silvery green groves of olive trees
which thrived in the unyielding soil.

Legends of their past abounded among the proud islanders.   They loved nothing better than when the
strange Englishman talked to them in the musical tones
of their own beautiful language.   Oh, yes, this man
surely knew much about their history—and they wondered at this.   Stories, familiar to them that had been
handed down from generation to generation, he knew
equally well.

Evans said: "Yes, indeed, I do believe perhaps Heinrich Schliemann was right."

They were standing at the edge of the site near Candia, known to the natives as *Makrotichos* ("Long Wall"). Here and there, outcroppings of ruined man-made stonework dotted the mound. "I feel sure that we are not looking at a natural mound. This mound is artificial. What, I wonder, would we find if we were to dig into it? Well, there is but one way to find out. Dig!"

Word spread like wildfire over the island. Some were pleased, seeing a prospect of work, others laughed. "The Englishman has bought the land outside Candia. He's going to dig it up!" Arguments at the small inns and cafés were furious and heated. Many summed up their thoughts thus: "That fool with the stick will have a hard summer's work when the weather gets hot!"

On March 23, 1900, having hired workmen to help him, Arthur Evans began to dig into the land he had purchased. He expected little except a pleasant summer, with the possibility of finding more of the charms he sought, perhaps a few broken pots. By summer's end, he would return to England.

Forty years later, Arthur Evans was still hard at work on the island of Crete!—for the spades had taken him backwards in time almost beyond human imagining.

The story of the persistent man, Arthur Evans, and the incredible Minoan civilization he brought to light, begins many years before those fateful days in 1900!

The Fool and His Stick

He knew, for instance, that the great god Zeus supposed to have been born in a cave way up on side of snow-capped Mount Ida. He knew, too, of legend of a great king, Minos, who was supposed to descended from Zeus. The legends and tales came eas from his tongue, and the natives heard them with d light.

Most often, however, the man preferred to be alon He was looking for something. Sometimes, he poke about with only a guide as his companion. Other times he stood for hours looking at what appeared to be a large mound a few miles from Candia. What was he looking for?

Arthur Evans was, indeed, looking for something. For several years he had been collecting seals and beads, which many native islanders, and others who lived on the Greek mainland, wore as good luck charms. These charms had often been passed down in families for untold generations. Arthur Evans frequently had difficulty buying them from people who were reluctant to part with their charms against evil. But times were hard and money was scarce, so the Englishman had built quite a collection.

The charms themselves held little monetary value for Arthur Evans. But they had another value for him. He had noticed the unusual inscriptions on them and had begun to evolve a theory of their possible meaning and significance. So, he was seeking more of them for study.

Speaking more to himself than to his guide, Arthur

TWO

"I Hope He Will Have Good Sense . . ."

> My baby has a good deal of the Dickinson in him, indeed, he
> has a double right to it, and I fear he inherits also a little of the
> Pepper, what your Father calls the "Volcanic" Nature, but as
> he has a very finely formed head and marked intelligent features
> I hope he will have good sense and then a great deal may be done
> by training. . . .

THUS WROTE Harriet Dickinson Evans, in 1851, upon the birth of her first child. Harriet and John Evans named the baby Arthur John, after his two grandfathers.

They lived in the house Harriet's tyrannical and unpredictable father had built for them. John Dickinson had brooked no interference from the young couple in the size, planning, or design of the house he insisted on building. The young people's courtship had been strained, for Harriet's father was an extremely wealthy man, having made a fortune in the paper-making industry. He was snobbish, and did not consider the young

John Evans a suitable match for his pretty daughter.

But John Evans was a man of strong character. He had known bitter disappointment, for he had been too poor to attend Oxford University, the school of his dreams. He had to go to work at the age of seventeen in his Uncle John Dickinson's paper mills. For his further education, he relied upon his own diligence and character.

Now, having long since left his home, Market Bosworth, in Leicestershire, England, John had established himself with great success in Hemel Hempstead, the home of the paper mills just outside London. He had worked hard and was regarded, even by old John Dickinson, as an important member of the firm. John Dickinson held many patents for paper-making machinery he had invented. John Evans, in his turn, was busy introducing new items for the firm to make. One of these was very important, the manufacture of envelopes.

The new baby, Arthur, had unusual objects of play from the beginning. As had his father and grandfather before him, Arthur Evans's toys consisted largely of paleolithic (stone age) and neolithic (new stone age) relics. The interest in these antiquities was a family trait, passed on from father to son, and nearly all the children remembered the ancient flint and stone objects with which they played.

During the next few years, Arthur was presented with two brothers and two sisters. Their home was filled with laughter, good conversation, music, and friends. There were lively discussions about ancient mankind, for the study of ancient man was an abiding passion of their father, John Evans. His work for the paper mills required him to travel, sometimes across to Europe, and thus he met men all over the Continent with similar interests. John Evans had successfully combined his tasks for his firm with his passionate pursuit of the relics of prehistoric mankind.

Men like John Evans pooled their knowledge and studies, thus spreading understanding. At the meetings of their learned societies, The Royal Society, The Society of Antiquaries, in England, and others in other countries, they presented their findings to like-minded researchers. The societies, exchanging information freely across national frontiers, served as a common meeting ground, a clearing house for this exchange of ideas and information.

The young years were happy ones for Arthur Evans. He could be a very solemn little boy, but generally he was cheerful and people responded to him. Not surprisingly, a few members of the family thought him a bit precocious, for he possessed a poise and intelligence beyond his tender years. Harriet refused to worry about it. She explained patiently: "The boy hears all kinds of stories when his father has visitors, because John never tells him to go away and play. He welcomes the boy's interest and company. No doubt, when he starts to school, he'll become a bit less reserved. However that may be, he's never any trouble to us."

There were good reasons for Arthur's reserve, for, unfortunately, Arthur Evans had inherited more than just
an intense interest in ancient history. He also suffered
a family trait of nearsightedness. This was one of the
main reasons he appeared reserved. The affliction was,
in some ways, a handicap. But it was very obvious to
Harriet and John that their son seldom let it bother him.
On the contrary, he quickly found that his trouble with
his eyes had distinct advantages. He discovered that he
could read tiny writing and copy it from his father's
collection of coins and medallions. Such details often
escaped the notice of people with normal eyesight unless
they used a powerful magnifying glass.

Time was passing its leisurely way. Arthur's father
had achieved prominence as a man of science and his
name was well known beyond the boundaries of England.

Many important discoveries were being made in caves
in France where paintings, tens of thousands of years
old were found. (Later discovery of four skeletons of
this early race of human beings established, by 1868, the
existence of Cro-Magnon man.) Whenever possible,
John Evans would visit the sites of such discoveries and
talk to the men who made them.

Returning from a trip to France one day, John Evans
saw young Arthur running to greet him. Clutching his
father's hand, Arthur danced along beside him. "Did
you have a good journey, Father?" The questions
tumbled from his lips so fast, he was breathless when
they reached the house. "Did you see anything interesting? Did you visit the caves in France?"

When the flurry and bustle of homecoming quieted, they settled in the parlor. Harriet, as interested as her son, sat sewing. Now and then she murmured to Arthur not to get so excited.

"Just imagine," John Evans began, "once upon a time, thousands of years ago, England was probably joined by some kind of land bridge to Europe. The white chalk cliffs between Dover and Calais have exactly the same geological strata construction. Long ago, people could walk back and forth freely where the English Channel now swells."

"Did mammoths and sabre-toothed tigers live in France, too, Father?" Arthur asked eagerly. "Were the relics you saw like those that have been found in England?"

"Yes," said John Evans. "They are definite links between the two countries. Perhaps, as the ice age retreated, the glaciers that had gouged great valleys in the earth, filled the valleys with water from melting snow and ice. Melting ice and snow must have played a part in shaping the earth as we know it. It seems very certain to me that the world was once a very different place than it is now."

He smiled at his open-mouthed son, who was drinking in every word. "Mankind," he went on, "is much older than some people realize. I'm sure of that. But we just don't know how old. For all we know there may have been several ice ages. The bones we've found prove that, at one time, huge wolves and sabre-toothed tigers lived in our part of the world. The debris of the caves, and the fossils found in mud flats, tell us that ancient peoples with only stone and flint weapons had mastery over these fearsome beasts."

"But what happened to all those animals?" Arthur wanted to know.

"Well, of course, we don't know the whole story yet," his father answered. "But from what we've seen, it would appear that those who did not follow the warm weather were trapped by the intense cold that descended upon their hunting grounds, and perished. Those that moved with the weather managed to survive and then slowly adapted to different conditions. Some of the animals succeeded in adapting to the cold, too, but there is so much we don't know. But isn't it wonderful trying to find out?"

Arthur nodded thoughtfully, cupping his chin in his hands.

"When we study the weapons and tools of prehistoric people," John Evans said, "pieces of a puzzle begin to fall into place. We begin to get a glimpse of the life and habits of these ancients, and pictures emerge which show us how different our country and our ancestors once were."

In the warmth of his family circle, Arthur Evans did not know that a dark cloud was moving across his horizon. A few days before Christmas, 1857, fate struck a blow from which Arthur never fully recovered.

Shortly after the birth of her second daughter, the beloved Harriet Evans became seriously ill. Unaware, the nurse who had attended her brought an infection to Harriet's childbed. Harriet fell victim immediately and grew steadily worse. Arthur and his brothers and sister, at this holiday season, were temporarily lost in the anxiety of their mother's sick room. Child though he was, Arthur Evans was afraid. He knew what was happening.

There was nobody with the thought, the understanding, or the time to comfort the unhappy boy. His grief, he soon learned, had to be private, to be borne as well as he could.

It was a dreadfully cold day when John Evans laid his wife in her last resting place. There could be no joy and festivity on the bleak New Year's day of 1858. John Evans was in abject despair. The future looked black. He had five children, including the new baby girl, to care for, yet he knew, despite his suffering, these children *must* be cared for and life *must* go on.

Missing Harriet terribly, John Evans browsed one day in his wife's diary. Scarcely thinking, he wrote a comment:

"The children do not seem to miss their mother."

Perhaps it was natural that his own grief blinded him to Arthur's need. The mills demanded constant attention, and he was so worried about the children and how to maintain a home for them that he failed to note their individual needs.

(Years later, when in his seventies, Arthur came across his father's note in Harriet's diary. Despite the great span of years, Arthur's grief remained so keen, that he scrawled a great big NO beside his father's comment.)

John Evans slowly pulled together the threads of his shattered life. His heart often ached, especially when he traveled and found the scenery lovely. How Harriet would have enjoyed it! Luckily for John and for his family, there was a young woman he had known for some time. Eventually, he turned to Fanny Phelps.

Fanny was a distant cousin and had been bridesmaid to Harriet. John proposed and, to his great joy, Fanny accepted. Everyone was pleased, including the children. Fanny was a young woman of charm and dignity and great good sense. The old Dickinsons welcomed her like a daughter. John Evans felt a great weight ease from his shoulders. In July, 1859, John Evans and Fanny Phelps were married.

Fanny could never take his mother's place in Arthur's heart, yet he loved her and she helped fill the void in his young life. Fanny was warm and feminine and it was good to be near her. Without fuss or bother, Fanny tackled the routine of raising Harriet's children. She proved to be a good homemaker and the companionship and love that grew strong between her and John enriched the lives of those about them.

Fanny was a great help to John in the preparation of his numerous scientific papers. She always had a ready ear for the children's troubles, a comforting hug for their misfortunes.

In the summer of 1860, time was drawing near for

Arthur to return to school. His father summoned him. "Arthur, how would you like to take a holiday with me before you start back to school?"

The boy was delighted. "Will you really take me? Just the two of us?"

"Of course. And I'll tell you something. At Dunwich, there was once a Roman encampment of some kind. I propose we go there, take a couple of spades, and see what we can find."

It was one of the best summers of Arthur's life. Busy and eager, he followed his father about the site of the old Roman settlement. Excited, he cried out when his spade struck something hard and he unearthed a bit of broken pottery. They found nothing of value or real importance, but it was a wonderful summer.

Arthur Evans had taken a small step toward his destiny.

John Evans, discussing Arthur's future with him one day, suggested he might like to enter the paper-making business. Arthur objected strenuously, for scholarship and learning were what he wanted about him all his life. He took financial security for granted. It was fortunate for him that his father's prosperity enabled him to do so. John Evans could afford to indulge his son where he, himself, had been denied. He did not try to force Arthur to a way of life he did not relish.

Arthur entered Harrow School, an aristocratic preparatory school, before entering Oxford University. He was

not particularly popular with his classmates in the beginning. Information he had mastered at his father's
knees was a complete mystery to many of his fellows, and
he was sometimes thought conceited because of his
knowledge. And knowing so much made him somewhat
lazy with his formal studies. He seemed shy, and his
nearsightedness made him carry his finely shaped head
at a peculiar angle. He looked like someone peering
constantly into secret places.

Arthur was not physically attractive. His frame was
small and his features undistinguished. Yet his stumbling
speech and simple sincerity charmed the few friends
he made and kept.

As his school fellows learned to understand him,
Arthur responded and became more at ease. He readily
entered into the activities of his school. He could not
play cricket because of his poor eyesight, but he refused
to let this stop him from playing Rugby football, a much
tougher game. He took his knocks, blows, and bruises
with the best of them.

Many of Arthur's lessons bored him, but he engaged
in school debates with great success. He began to write
stories, satires on the school and its best-known figures,
and he wrote witty poetry. Gradually, he became known
as a good fellow, an interesting companion.

Arthur finally endeared himself to his fellow students
—and annoyed some of his professors!—with a published
satirical letter in the *Harrovian,* a school paper he helped
to found and jointly edit. In the guise of advising new

students, the letter poked fun at the standards of some of the teachers. Arthur Evans offered the following suggestions: "The first great thing you should do is to be as noisy as you can. That pays more than anything; and if you carry it out well, you are sure to be popular. Then you shouldn't be squeamish about telling a few lies to masters, if you have occasion. . . . Then you should talk as much slang as possible, and perhaps the best way of getting that up is to read through as many two-shilling novels as possible, but don't get any of Thackeray's, or Dickens', or Scott's, or that style of book. . . . Besides you should get books where lots of Dukes and Marquises and that sort of people are brought in—it looks swell you know. . . ."

During these days, Arthur's eye bothered him. Winter was the hardest time of all, and early twilights were hard on his eyes. When there was no friend to lead him, Arthur blundered and wandered his own way. Glasses would have helped, but he would not wear them regularly. His eyesight became a very real problem, but he solved it in his own stubborn way.

Arthur acquired a walking stick! Promptly, he named it "Prodger," and he was never again without it. "Prodger" seemed to have a personality all its own. Arthur did not use it only as a walking stick, but also to poke into things he couldn't quite make out. He loped along, lost in his own thoughts, waving "Prodger" wildly around his head.

Many an amusing story grew up about "Prodger."

There were those who thought he used the excuse of poor eyesight for his own purposes; he could see well enough, they maintained, how else could he spy a friend across the street? Oblivious of the shouts and yells from carriage drivers, as he hastily stopped traffic, Arthur waved "Prodger" in the air, tramped across the street to his friend and strode on his way, quite unaware of the havoc he left behind!

In his last days at Harrow, Arthur came into his own. The publication of more satires and poems drew attention to him. At seventeen, in 1869, he became secretary to the Scientific Society, and exhibited some of his own collection of antiquities. He wrote a study of Antiquity in Men which was well received, and enjoyed at school.

Arthur also had a good sense of humor. He often disturbed his whole class with his pranks. As soon as he was seated, whispers swept the room. What new trick was Evans up to now?

"Pssst! Look at Evans!" Stifled laughter shook the boys. They tried to look around, keeping an eye upon the teacher. "He's got a snake!"

There sat Arthur, quietly urging his pet grass snake up his shirt sleeve! It was very difficult for the boys to muffle their laughter when, on command, Arthur had the snake poke its head out his shirt collar!

THREE

Adventures of the Young Man

IN 1870, Arthur Evans entered Brasenose College, Oxford University. Though his interest was in Ancient History, no such courses were then offered at Oxford. He could continue with the study of Latin and Greek, and thereby read the ancient historians' works; but he could not "major" in Ancient History. So Arthur chose Modern History, the next best thing. And at once, he found himself in a peculiar state of mind, both pleased and vexed.

Unlike his father at the same age, Arthur was well off financially. Having known nothing different, he took security as his due. Yet he was grateful and handled his money with care. There was much, he reflected, to be pleased about. But though on the threshold of preparation for his future, he had no clear purpose.

In his own person, many fine qualities were develop-

ing. Arthur was kind, and tremendously aware of the
world about him. But the sense of purpose eluded him.
Should he aim at teaching? What about the ministry,
politics, letters? He had many interests and knew many
subjects well, but which did he wish to follow? Archaeology was his deep and sustaining love, yet Oxford offered
little in archaeological studies, for the science was in its
infancy.

In his half-lazy manner, Arthur drifted with the tide.
Now and then he nibbled at a subject that caught his
fancy, but nothing really gripped his imagination and
filled the need for a purpose.

The scholastic reputation of Arthur's father, mean-
while, continued to grow. Honors came to him frequently. But Arthur was not content to be known as the
son of a great and famous man. "I know as well as anyone else," he said, "that my father is a great man. I'm
pleased and proud to be his son. But why do people always call me 'little Evans,' the son of John Evans the
great!"

Arthur Evans was sincere when he told friends how
delighted he was with his father's fame, but he did not
wish to bask in his father's reflected glory. Deep inside,
he knew the challenge of his father's accomplishments
called for him to respond. But how? He had a strong
urge to make his own mark, make *his* contribution to the
world.

As the pleasant years slipped by, Arthur seemed to
have little to show for what effort he made in his studies.
But he was not particularly concerned. Lightheartedly,

he made plans for a summer vacation. With his brother, Lewis, he decided on a walking tour of France, a very bold thing to do in 1871!

Europe lagged behind England in industrialization. One traveled, for the most part, by coach or horseback, or on foot. Exaggerated notions of living conditions on the Continent existed among the staid folk of Victorian England. Accommodation was poor, they said. Drinking water was dangerous and bad. And at every turn there was someone waiting to rob the unwary traveler.

None of this made the slightest impression upon Arthur. He was young and full of life. He knew that others had ventured across the English Channel, and had fallen in love with what they found. Everything on the Continent seemed gay and colorful. The people seemed to enjoy life more. What if some things *were* crude? To a young man filled with the spirit of adventure, it meant nothing.

Arthur Evans collected an outfit he considered suitable for traveling abroad. His father and Fanny were aghast when he came home with one of his prizes. Laughing and bowing, capering about the room, Arthur exhibited a choice item. "Well," he cried, "how do you like it?"

"I simply cannot imagine, Arthur, what you want with a thing like that!" his father grunted.

"Arthur, it's frightful!" Fanny said with a smile.

Unruffled, Arthur still laughed. "All the best travelers have one," he said. "It has a thousand and one purposes."

Gaily he pranced about his brother, enfolding him in

the immense, scarlet-lined black cape he'd been showing off. "Now," he said, "aren't I dashing and gallant?"

"I think you look more like an anarchist," his father replied.

When Arthur and his brother landed in France, tension knifed the air. Prussian soldiers occupied much of France at this time, including Paris. The continent was in a high state of unrest. Arthur admired the bearing of the Prussian soldiers who were everywhere. It suited his romantic nature very well. Luckily for him, however, he immediately ran into a man whose opinion gave him pause. Arthur was perched on a bench, one leg dangling, when an official approached.

"Non, M'sieur," said the French customs officer, pointing to Arthur's great cape with its brilliant red lining.

Arthur, with "Prodger" perched on his shoulder like a rifle, was puzzled. "What is it?" he said with some irritation.

"M'sieur," said the customs man, "do you not realize we have been at war? The country is occupied by the Prussians and the times are dangerous!"

"What has that to do with me?" Arthur wanted to know. "I am an Englishman! Nobody would dare bother me!"

The customs man smiled. He had long experience with these proud and eccentric Englishmen from across the Channel. They thought they owned the world. And for all their oddity, he liked them. He fingered Arthur's great cloak. "If the Prussians see you wearing this, they will think you are a spy. They will shoot you like a dog!" His eyes twinkled. "And, M'sieur," he went on, "can a *dead Englishman* argue with bullets?"

Arthur, partly scared, partly annoyed, wisely followed the officer's advice. It was a big disappointment, but he laid the scarlet-lined cloak inside his bag.

Once through customs, Arthur Evans felt an intoxicating sense of freedom. Eyes alert, he drew in the alien sights and sounds and smells. Every minute was packed with excitement. He and his brother occasionally broke the round of sightseeing by calling upon a friend of their father's. The conversation during these visits, the exchange of information on French and English stone-age discoveries, added zest to the trip for Arthur. Lewis Evans was not so interested, but both young men were surprised to learn how many people in this foreign land knew and respected their father. Lewis agreed to visit the caves at Dordogne and see the prehistoric paintings that were recently found there.

Arthur had his full share of youthful bumptiousness, and had a ready opinion about almost everything. After a special visit to the French National Assembly, which was meeting at Versailles, he said to Lewis: "Well, I don't think much of them. It's no wonder the Prussians have conquered France. These deputies have no discipline. One would think they have no respect for law and order at all!"

Tramping the roads of France, the youths crossed into and explored parts of Germany. Neither of them spoke

German, but they got along, making their wants known with Latin.

And then, finally, they set foot in the Balkans. Instantly Arthur was captivated. His wildest imaginations could not have conjured up more colorful, exotic surroundings, or a more fascinating and provocative people. Arthur Evans lost his heart to the area which had once been known as the ancient province of Illyria. This ancient province, ill defined, stretching back from the coast of Dalmatia, was dotted with ancient Greek and Roman remains.

Arthur bought a complete Turkish outfit on the very first day, and spent most of the remainder of his money in noisy, humming bazaars.

A more vivid contrast between the scenes that met his gaze in southeastern Europe and the drabness he thought of as England, could not be imagined. Here, on the soil of Illyria, all was life and color and movement. The animated faces of the different races of people enchanted him. Even their houses were painted bright colors. The fierce and prideful appearance of the people, the strange gaiety of their dress, drew forth the poetry of Arthur's soul. He was entranced by the contrast of onion-domed churches of the Eastern Orthodox Christian faith, with slender minareted mosques of the Moslems. He was astounded to find that many of these religious shrines rested upon foundations of buildings that had been old at the time of the Romans.

On his return to England, Arthur was appalled to dis-

cover how very little had been published in England
concerning the lands and peoples he had just visited.

"The ignorance here at home about the Balkans,
Father," he said, "is shocking!"

John Evans contented himself by nodding agreement.

"I shall write about this trip. At least, if I get it published, it will do a little to fill the gap."

True to his words, Arthur wrote an article, a full
account of his journeys of 1871. It was eventually published in *Frazer's Magazine,* in May, 1873, under the
title, "Over the Marches of Civilized Europe."

Arthur kept another promise he made himself. He
continued traveling. During the next four years, he
spent each summer and shorter holidays, tramping
throughout Europe. He penetrated into the far north of
Lapland, where few travelers ventured, and he crossed
the length and breadth of Europe.

From each of his trips to the Balkans, Arthur returned
with more pottery and ancient coins. It intrigued him
how designs, often going back to ancient Greece and
Rome, had recurred, generation after generation, in the
utensils of these peoples, and were still popular and
practical. These threads, weaving their way through
the tapestry of human existence, fascinated him.

After each trip, Arthur returned to Oxford more dis-
contented than ever. He found it hard to concentrate,
for his heart remained in the warm southlands of the
Continent.

One summer, Arthur set out for Europe with his

younger brother, Phillip Norman. They headed straight
for Rumania. Arthur was well equipped with notebooks
and pencils.

"Heavens!" Norman said. "Why do you want to cart
all that stuff about?"

"You'll see!" Arthur replied. "I'm going to en-
lighten our countrymen about true conditions over here.
They're so ill informed, and I think I can change all
that!"

Nothing unusual befell the young men on the way to
Budapest, but continuing to Petrosani and wilder country, their sense of excitement grew. Typically, they had
not bothered with passports or official identity papers, so
an element of danger added spice to their travels.

"My word," Norman said to his brother when they
found themselves in a crowd of peasants journeying the
same way. "How they stink of garlic!"

But Arthur saw beyond the obvious. He took notes on
the physical characteristics of the people, wondering and
speculating about their origins. Fierce looking peasants,
with great black eyes and bushy black moustaches, seemed
to Arthur the wildest looking people he had ever met.
Magyars, Wallachians, and Germans jostled each other
on the streets.

Arthur's letters home were full of stories about these
people. He described some of them wearing great sheep-
skin cloaks and jackets. Perhaps, he thought, all of them
have a common slavic origin. Their haunting and lively
folk dancing and the strange rhythms of their music
warmed and excited him.

Beyond Petrosani, the two young men turned aside into the foothills and mountains. They had nothing but a map and a compass. They had a small stock of food in their knapsacks, bread and jam and sausage. They did not know even whether there was a pass across the jagged rocks. Blithely, they set out into the unknown.

On and up they climbed, passing very few signs of human habitation. Toward nightfall there was not a sign of another human being. Then, just before darkness closed in, they met a band of Wallachian peasants. They proved most friendly. It was hard to converse with them, since the peasants understood no English. Fortunately, they managed to get along once more by using Latin and a few words of Italian.

Cheerfully, the peasants invited the young men to spend the night at their camp.

The stark simplicity of the lives of these people amazed Arthur. They did not bother with tea, coffee, or sugar. Their flocks of sheep and goats provided all their needs from shoe leather to cheese. Their camp proved to be a rough kind of tent, like a wigwam. Skins were stretched over poles, and inside it was snugly floored with thick sheepskins. A roaring fire was soon blazing outside the tent.

Arthur watched as they prepared their scant evening meal. One huge peasant tossed a hunk of salt-covered fungus of some kind into the fire. When it was cooked, he took a piece of rough grained black bread from his pocket and settled down to munch the fungus and bread. He laughed at Arthur's close interest.

"Ecco la!" ("Here!") he said, tossing Arthur a piece of the fungus. *"E buono!"* ("It's good.")

Without a moment's hesitation, Arthur bit into the offered morsel. *"Si, è buono."* He smiled at the peasant. "It tastes wonderfully good," he said to his brother. His obvious enjoyment pleased the peasant who smiled back at him before crawling to his place in the tent.

Unfortunately for Arthur and his brother, there was no room for them in the tent. They made themselves as comfortable as they could on the straw mattresses the peasants offered, and settled down beside the fire. No sooner had they begun to relax than it started to rain. It was a wretched night. The rain soaked them, so they got up to dry beside the fire. And when they tried to lie down again, they found their straw beds soaked.

Huddling around the hissing fire, Arthur and Norman were glad to see the first streaks of dawn brighten the eastern sky. Before it was fully light, they had eaten their breakfast and were on their way in a northeasterly direction.

"My word, Arthur!" Norman called. "Look at this!"

Arthur trotted to his brother's side. There, unmistakably outlined in the sticky mud, were the footprints of a bear!

"I'm glad we haven't run into Mr. Grizzly yet," Arthur said, trying to make light of the matter.

Soon the young men were hopelessly lost. There were, however, more signs of humanity, and from time to time they met other peasants. As well as they could make themselves understood, the peasants gave directions and the young men continued on.

After two sleepless nights they had to get some rest. Footsore and weary, they descended a steep hillside to the valley below where they had seen a stream bubbling a silvery way down the valley. Looking around, they found a rock shelter, a kind of shallow cave. It looked wonderful, as if it had been made especially for them. Gratefully, they settled themselves into the cave, spreading their things, and got ready to sleep.

Arthur scrunched himself down into the hard ground. He was just about to drop off to sleep when a startled hiss awakened him.

"Arthur!" his brother whispered in a voice filled with alarm.

"What is it?" Arthur found himself whispering in response.

"Over there, look!" Norman indicated some bushes, trying not to be obvious. "There are two men hiding in those bushes watching us. *They have guns!*"

The villainous looking men did not know they had been seen. While the youths watched, the men sneaked from the bushes and moved to another hiding place *nearer* the shelter where Norman and Arthur crouched. Though they had been lucky in avoiding trouble so far, both boys knew that brigands infested these wild hills. Murders and robberies were common.

Whispering, the young men took stock of their situation. "They evidently plan to wait until they think we are asleep," Arthur said. "Let's get our things back into the packs. As soon as we're ready, we'll toss a heap of this wet wood on the fire. We can escape behind the smoke screen."

"I'm glad we had sense enough to gather the wood before we settled down," his brother whispered gratefully.

Quickly, they stuffed their gear into their packs. Then, while the fire poured out great plumes of smoke, they crept behind it and away from where the two men with guns sat waiting. The ruse succeeded, and they were relieved to find they were not being followed.

"I hate to think what might have happened if we hadn't got away," Norman said thankfully.

A few days later, successfully dodging border guards, they left Rumania and began their trek home.

Arthur was rapidly educating himself to things he could not learn at school. Few travelers had covered as much ground as he had in these summers. But the days were flying by, and almost before he realized it, the time was at hand for examinations and graduation.

Whatever else he lacked, Arthur Evans did not lack self-discipline. The last summer of his four years at Oxford, 1874, he realized he had a lot of work to do if he were to graduate. Oxford would not accept his second best. Arthur threw himself into a summer of intense study. He worked very hard and was rewarded in December when he was graduated with first class honors. He felt gratified, yet he was also honest enough to admit that he could have done even better.

The year 1874 saw Gladstone, one of Arthur's heroes, out of power, Disraeli once again Prime Minister. Arthur's father now moved in and out of government circles, law circles, science and literary circles with the greatest of ease. The topics he discussed with his friends were discussed at home. Disraeli, now a Victorian aristocrat, believed, "The world is for the few . . . the *very* few." This attitude was to cost his country dearly.

John Evans tended to be conservative. He believed in peace and prosperity, and was glad to see Disraeli back at the head of England's affairs. Some of the "radical" ideas that Gladstone and his party were trying to bring into being were anathema to him.

Arthur Evans was the opposite of his father in some ways. He welcomed all that Gladstone stood for. Ideas and ideals were Arthur's food and drink. Arthur's liberal attitude toward life led him to champion minorities who suffered oppression. The differences between father and son were profound, but typical of their changing days.

Arthur felt no inferiority to his father. Far from it. They were close and shared their ideas and thoughts freely. The younger man was keenly aware of his own talents, but he had to find an occupation worthy of them.

The stirring of new ideas, the seething unrest in the Balkans, seemed to beckon Arthur Evans with a promise that there he might find himself.

FOUR

Newspaperman

IN APRIL of 1875, Arthur was glad to be headed once more toward the Balkans. Before going south, he tarried a while at Gottingen in Germany. Here he found the students were allowed to prepare dissertations on almost any subject, unlike Oxford where subjects were limited. Delighted with this attitude, at first, Arthur settled into the university routine.

There were, he discovered rapidly, many wide differences between the methods of education. While Oxford might limit subject matter, its standards were very high and difficult to attain.

"How," he asked another English student one day "can our tutor here in Germany lecture to us on the Anglo-Saxons? Not only has he never been to England—he doesn't even speak English!" He tossed his head angrily. "It's as bad as if I set myself up as a Russian expert, not knowing the language or having experienced anything about the country and the people!"

July came and he shook the dull dust of Gottingen from his feet, glad to get on to Herzegovina, in the Balkans. This time, Arthur came prepared. He carried a Bosnian vocabulary, money tables, and notes on the history, racial background, dress, and customs relating to the various races he hoped to study.

It was well that he came prepared, for the moment twenty-four-year-old Arthur stepped across the frontier, he stepped into the heart of a violent revolution!

Since 1463, Bosnians, Albanians, Dalmatians, Croatians, Serbians, and other races had been under Turkish yoke. In 1699, the major powers of Europe acknowledged Turkish suzerainty in the lands they had conquered.

Now, corruption had eaten deep into the heart of the Ottoman Empire. The captive peoples of Turkey's European lands were flexing their muscles, girding for the struggle for independence from foreign masters. The smouldering fires had burst into flame at Herzegovina. On the sidelines, Austria and Russia and Prussia watched and waited, each alert to jump, for her own expansion, when Turkey seemed weak enough.

In England, where so little was known about the Balkan peoples, some individuals tried to alert the government to the dangers of the situation, but the authorities seemed content merely to observe. Those who warned of impending disaster were unheeded.

Arthur found much that he liked and respected in Turkish culture. Inevitably, however, his idealism placed him squarely on the side of the harassed minority. He did not actively take up arms and start fighting. But finally, though realization was slow coming, he had found a cause. He was not afraid to air his views. He argued his points at every chance. Arthur Evans believed the Balkan peoples (most of whom now make up modern Yugoslavia) should have their freedom.

The seething pot of racial hatreds boiled on, growing more turbulent each day.

The ancient land of Illyria delighted Arthur. He prowled the streets and markets in search of old coins and anything else he could find to help in his historical study. He copied inscriptions from buildings and monuments; mosques and churches which still bore carved writings that had been made centuries before. What a delight it would be, he thought, if only it were possible to excavate around the bases of some of these buildings. He discovered several tantalizing mounds and felt sure these were neolithic burial mounds.

On the way to Sarajevo, capital of Serbia, Arthur met an Englishwoman, Miss Irby. This casual meeting was to draw Arthur into the heart of the revolt.

"You're English, aren't you?" Miss Irby inquired of the young man.

"Yes, I am," Arthur acknowledged. He introduced himself, and they talked pleasantries of England for a while. Traveling down the river Sava, Arthur learned a good deal about the Balkans from Miss Irby.

"The atrocities going on out here," she told him, "are simply awful. Turks and Christians cut each other's throats on the slightest pretext. Such senseless killings! Where will it all end?"

She explained, "I operate a girls' school in Sarajevo. I'm on my way there now. I'm sure this is only the beginning of serious fighting, so I must hurry and get my girls moved to the safety of Belgrade. They should be all right there, at least until I know how this is all going to end."

"And shall you stay in Belgrade, then?" Arthur asked.

"I really don't know, Mr. Evans. One cannot stand idly by and see such suffering without trying to help. The terror, the poverty and starvation is shocking. Refugees are swarming everywhere. It is the children I worry about most. Hundreds of them are nothing more than walking bags of bones!

"I've managed to raise some money and supplies in England for relief," she went on. "But it's very little. The people at home simply don't know what's happening here. It's all so foreign to them, so far away. I'm sure if they only knew, if they could see the things I've seen, they'd come to our aid."

Arthur agreed. Here was a cause that began to set his imagination working. Miss Irby's tales of atrocities chilled his blood, and Arthur did not question the veracity of her information. He turned the alarming situation over in his mind and looked about him with greater keenness.

Arthur had mixed feelings as his journey continued.

He was intensely angry over the tales Miss Irby related. His senses of justice and decency were outraged. And yet the beauty of the country provided sharp contrast to its misery. The great onion-domed churches, richly decorated, rose up on the skyline of Brod. In the red-gold light of dawn, muezzins stepped on to the small balconies of mosques. Cupping hands to their mouths, they sang the praises of Allah and called the Moslem faithful to prayer. Their chanting canopied the roofs of Brod. All seemed serene and peaceful.

In the streets, as the city woke to life for another day, riots of color were loosed. Christians and Moslems mingled in the market places. Hatred or no, life must go on. Bright turbans bobbed amongst red-fezzed Moslem men and black-veiled Moslem women. The gaudy, barbaric costumes of Serbians and Croatians seemed in themselves explosive. But now, Arthur saw more than these things. One scarcely walked a few hundred yards without hearing a heated quarrel. Normal trade haggling was touched with bitterness.

When Arthur set foot ashore at Brod, he was immediately arrested as a "Russian spy"! Miss Irby's remonstrances were brushed aside. In truth, the troops of the Austrian Emperor who arrested him had no business in the country at all. Their pretext for being there was to "restore peace and maintain order" until the fate of the strife-ridden lands was settled.

Fortunately, this time Arthur had his passport. Indignant, bristling with anger, "Prodger" waving around his head, he protested his arrest. He talked sternly in a loud voice, quelling his captors until they grew nervous, demanding justice. He demanded to see the highest officer present. The vehemence of his protest did not prevent him from being thrown into a prison cell—without "Prodger." Yet his protestations had made an impression. Half an hour later, his release was ordered by an apologetic Austrian captain.

Appalled at such high-handed treatment, Arthur was anxious to get into Turkish-held territory. But there was a problem. Dervish Pasha, Governor of Bosnia, had declared martial law. All movements were restricted. Few were being allowed over the frontier without special passes. Bands of wild rebels patrolled unguarded places. Arthur went from official to official seeking permission to cross the frontier. Wishing him luck in his efforts, Miss Irby hurried on to Sarajevo and her girls. Finally, Arthur succeeded in getting a pass from the Turkish governor himself!

Arriving at Sarajevo, he was distressed to learn that the revolt was spreading rapidly—so much so, he was almost a prisoner within the city. The populace was panic stricken. A huge fire had been set, which burned down much of the Christian quarter. Christians, fearing more Turkish reprisals for the revolt, murdered Moslems. For a long time they had hidden behind the protection of foreign consulates; now they had lost hope that the consulates would protect them.

In all this strife, Arthur found the British consulate

at Sarajevo an island of peace and quiet, strangely com-
placent. He decided to stay there for a while. Now he
heard the other side of the story, discovering the consul to
be friendly with the Turks. He told Arthur tales of
atrocities committed against the Turks.

"Your attitude," Arthur told the consul, "seems a bit
onesided to me. I've heard far more concerning the
sufferings of Christians."

The consul was unimpressed by his young country-
man. "What do you know of what is happening here?
What do you know of the real situation?"

"I've nothing against individual Turks," Arthur replied. "In fact, those I have met treated me with as great
kindness and courtesy as any Christian. There can never
be any justification for the terror that exists here, nor the
crimes being committed daily, however. And I'll tell
you this, unless drastic reforms are made, and made at
once, the day of the Turk in these lands is over!"

Arthur's sympathy for the rebels did not endear him
to the consul. However, one point in the consul's remarks had struck home. He had, indeed, learned much
of the country's past, but he really knew little of its present. It was by chance he had stumbled into this fiery
situation. He had not sought it, nor had he realized how
deeply he cared for the struggle of these peoples.

Arthur Evans, while searching for coins and pottery,
prowled the streets. Using his archaeological interest
as an excuse, he talked to everyone, often losing himself
in the narrow alleys of the worst and most dangerous

districts.   He gathered a store of evidence which he sub-
stantiated whenever possible.   What he found sickened
him.   And his activities, as he should have known,
aroused suspicion.

The Austrian consul, watching events closely for his
Emperor, became convinced that Arthur's prowling was
not for archaeology and history.   This man was certain
that Arthur was a paid agitator sent by the British government.   Arthur was to discover, to his cost, that the
Austrians had long memories!

After several days, the British consul sighed with relief
when his unwelcome guest set out from Sarajevo to make
his way to the Adriatic coast.   Arthur loaded his knap-
sack with food before setting out on foot from the city.
He had no fear of falling in with bands of rebels because
he considered himself on their side.   Along his way he
saw knots of fleeing refugees, and once almost fell over
the cruelly mutilated body of a Christian.   He had no
more trouble after this and got through to ancient Ragusa (modern Dubrovnik).   And Arthur Evans strode
into his paradise—a paradise that was to become his
for more than seven years.

As Arthur was slowly drawn into the vortex of Balkan
politics, realization began to dawn of the hypnotic effect
this ancient Adriatic city held over him.   Its setting by
the sea, its gray stone, red-roofed architecture, were undeniably beautiful.   Ragusa had a very ancient history
and had once been a Venetian Republic.   The city was

full of relics of a glorious past, enough to gladden the
heart of the most avid historian. This past was alive and
vibrant to Arthur. But, much as he loved the old city,
by September, he decided to return to England.

Lewis had gone to work at the paper mills. Arthur's
sisters and Norman were in school. What should he do?

The need to organize his life seldom left Arthur. How
was he to pull the loose threads of his interests into one
strong cord? Though graduate work seemed uninviting,
he tried hard to get fellowships in some of the colleges at
Oxford, but each time he failed. He published a few
more articles on his travels and worked on his notes for a
book.

Fanny Phelps was a great help to her stepson in preparing his book for publication. By midsummer of 1876,
Arthur's book was published by Longman's. The book
bore a ponderous title, a fashion of the day: *Through
Bosnia and the Herzegovina on Foot, During the Insur-
rection, August and September 1875, with an Historical
Review of Bosnia and a Glimpse of the Croats, Slavonians
and the Ancient Republic of Ragusa.*

When the book came out, Arthur was roaming through
Norway and Sweden. He returned to find his book a
popular success, despite its title. And he had gained a
reputation as a Balkan expert. As fate would have it,
the Balkan pot was boiling fiercely once again, and Arthur's book helped many people in England to understand what was happening, and cleared some of the

tangled issues. Members of Parliament used the book as a basis for their points of view.

Questions were debated in Parliament based on Arthur's book. Gladstone made good use of his copy when he badgered Disraeli's cabinet for lack of policy.

In the midst of this uproar, another event, far more significant to Arthur's future, burst upon a startled world. Not more than a few years earlier, the fabulous eccentric, Heinrich Schliemann, had jolted disbelieving scholars by proving the existence of Troy. Now he had done it again!

Born of poor parents, Heinrich Schliemann had been on his own since the age of eleven. He had been shipwrecked, often hungry, but had educated himself and taught himself many languages, including Russian. He had built himself a vast fortune, much of it trading in dyestuffs in Russia, some made in California during the Gold Rush. Throughout his life, Schliemann had never forgotten the thrilling story Homer told in the Iliad. This story had been his secret delight since he was seven years old. Most scholars were inclined to believe that the tales were myths created by the master poet and story-teller, Homer; but Schliemann believed the stories of the battles of Greeks and Trojans on the plains outside the great city of Troy, and had vowed, as a boy, to find Troy.

When middle-aged, Heinrich Schliemann set out to prove his belief in Homer. And he actually discovered fabulous treasures of gold and unearthed the long buried city of Troy. Schliemann astounded those who had considered him a mere eccentric, and is often called the "father of archaeology."

Once more relying upon the veracity of Homer, Schliemann discovered ancient Mycenae. The Greek civilization, of which Mycenae was but a scrap, was far older than classic Greece. But very little was known about this earlier Greece.

Schliemann stumbled upon graves containing gold face masks and astonishing jewels. Mysterious seal rings and beads with strange inscriptions were found. Depicted upon these seals and beads were signs and symbols of a people previously unknown.

The treasures Schliemann was allowed to keep by the Greek government were exhibited, and John Evans and Arthur had many lively discussions on their significance.

The world of scholars pursuing the budding science of archaeology was so small that John Evans, well known himself, knew Heinrich Schliemann.

"People are saying," John Evans commented to his son, "that Schliemann can smell gold."

"I know, father, and I think that's a bit unkind," Arthur replied.

"There's no doubt Schliemann's on to something terribly important," John Evans said.

"It looks as if what he's found is far older than classic Greece," Arthur said. "I wonder what the meaning is of the inscriptions on those seals and beads? What on earth can the figure eight shield signify? They don't seem to be Greek. I certainly would like to examine some of them more closely myself."

Arthur got his chance later to examine the beads and seals, the masks and gold cups. He found the beads and jewels most fascinating. His nearsighted eyes seemed to bore into the pictographs and symbols he saw on these objects. Obviously, these must have belonged to a people about whom the world knew nothing. A glimmer of intuition flashed for a moment in Arthur's mind. He said nothing, but he began to feel sure that the odd signs and symbols must be some kind of writing.

Then the archaeologist in him was subdued for a while. He met Miss Irby again, and the die was cast. She was in London collecting funds and supplies for refugees. Arthur could not ignore her appeal. Interest in Schliemann's finds passed to the back of his mind. He joined the relief organization as its secretary, glad for the chance to go back to Ragusa and help "his" people.

Chance now thrust another opportunity upon him which he could not deny.

Through a friend, Arthur had been introduced to Mr. C. P. Scott, editor of *The Guardian*, Manchester, England. Then, as now, *The Guardian* was regarded as one of the world's greatest newspapers. The paper's policy was pro-Gladstone, anti-Disraeli. This suited Arthur, and Mr. Scott thought the young man fitted into his plans nicely. Scott was also a shrewd businessman

as well as a fine editor.   He concluded an agreement with
Arthur, knowing the young man was returning to the
Balkans.   He suggested that Arthur become special correspondent to the paper on Balkan affairs.   The paper
would pay the cost of all dispatches as well as the price
of individual stories it used.   But Arthur got no regular
salary.   Mr. Scott thought he'd made a profitable agreement.

Arthur did not concern himself with lack of salary.
He was delighted to have secured an outlet for his knowledge and views in such a great newspaper.

In January, 1877, now twenty-six years old, Arthur
Evans was back in Ragusa.   He had a real assignment
now, and he carried money and supplies for Miss Irby's
relief organization.   He helped distribute the relief and
learned all he could of the methods and purposes of
relief work.

Then, Arthur began to ferret out the truth about the
stories he heard.

FIVE

Truth Has a Price

ARTHUR EVANS was shocked and horrified by what he found. Anger spiced his reports, and Mr. Scott was delighted with the material which began to reach *The Guardian*.

On February 28, 1877, *The Guardian* published this dispatch:

I have never come in contact with so much human misery before. They crowded round us, these pinched haggard faces, these lean bony frames, scarred by disease and bowed down with hunger; they followed till it seemed a dreadful dance of death. There was one lad of twelve, as pale as a spectre, who could not live many hours; and by him another younger child, whose only clothing was a few rags held together and eked out by long tresses of a woman's hair.... We now crossed the Bosnian frontier, and followed a path which Uzèlatz (a Bosnian rebel chief) himself had constructed along a precipitous mountain steep...and presently found an old Bosnian, who guided us by more difficult mountain paths to a lonely glen, where a torrent divides the

Austrian from Bosnian territory, and where, on the Christian
side, we descried a series of caves in the rocky mountain side, to
which we now made our way. Then indeed broke upon my sight
such a depth of human misery as it has perhaps fallen to the lot
of few living men to witness. We crossed a small frozen cataract,
and passed the mouths of two lesser caverns, toothed with icicles
three feet long and over, and then we came to the mouth of a
large cave, a great black opening in the rock, from which as we
climbed up to it, crawled forth a squalid and half-naked swarm
of women, children and old men with faces literally eaten away
with hunger and disease. A little way off was another smaller
hole outside which leant what had once been a beautiful girl,
and inside, amidst filth and squalor which I cannot describe,
dimly seen through smoke and darkness, lay a woman dying of
typhus. Others crowded out of black holes and nooks, and I
found that there were about thirty in this den. . . . Another with
about a dozen, and then another more horrible than any. A
black hole, sloping downwards at so steep an angle as made
climbing up or down a task of some difficulty, descended thus
abruptly about thirty feet, and then seemed to disappear into
the bowels of the earth. The usual haggard crowd swarmed out
of the dark and foetid recesses below and crawling from an under-
ground lurking place at the bottom of the pit, there stumbled
into the light an old man, so lean, so wasted, with such hollow
sunken eyes, that he seemed nothing but a walking skeleton; it
was the realization of some ghastly medieval picture of the resur-
rection of the dead. He seemed to have lost his reason, from below he stretched out his bony hands towards us as if to grasp
our alms, and made a convulsive effort to climb the rocky walls
of his den. He raised himself with difficulty, a few feet, and then
fell backward exhausted. . . .

This message, typical of many, aroused anger and controversy in England. There were many who challenged
the truth of Arthur Evans's reports, but he was not to be
outwitted or shouted down. He did not care how high a

price he paid for truth now that his own anger at such brutality was aroused. He investigated personally and collected names of witnesses and victims; the details of his reports were undeniably true.

Arthur and his stick, "Prodger," soon became familiar on the streets of Ragusa. Villagers smirked or smiled in affection as he strode by waving his stick. It was whispered from one to the other: "There goes the mad Englishman! He is an agent of milord Gladstone! Every night the rebel chiefs go to his house and he gives them bags of gold!"

Arthur paid no heed, but went on with his job, giving relief and investigating the horrible stories. He, and the wagon loads of supplies, were often turned back by Turks and forced to take hard mountain trails to reach their destination.

It was true enough he had many suspicious-looking night visitors at his lodgings. Some of these were rebels who brought him information for his stories. They knew he was a friend with a powerful voice in England. But most of the strange visitors, knowing his great interest in old things, were simply bringing antique coins, bits of carving and pottery they hoped to sell him.

In England, influential men who had faith in Evans's reports began to gather around and lend support. One of these, the historian, E.A. Freeman, now sided with the young reporter. He had passed through the Balkans himself when gathering material for a history of Sicily. A correspondence developed between the two men. Freeman's interest and friendship grew, and proved to be of profound importance to Arthur Evans.

In March of 1877, just before he left Ragusa to check a story of Turkish outrage against the small town of Ochievo, Arthur wrote to Freeman. He advised him of his coming journey and the grave danger that he might not return.

The area was terribly dangerous. Bands of rebels and soldiers hunted each other in the wild hills and mountains. It was a brooding, strange land through which Arthur now passed. Villagers warned him against the vampires which haunted the churchyards, and they told eerie tales of magic springs whose waters gave knowledge and cures for disease. They tried desperately to dissuade this stranger who was their friend from going on. Arthur persisted. The villagers warned him of dangerous river crossings, the river was now in flood from torrential rains and melting snows, but still Arthur pressed on.

Arthur stared at the raging river when he reached its banks. It looked cold enough; hunks of ice floated in it. He wandered up and down the bank but found no place to cross. He was all alone. Pondering for a moment, he frowned, then muttered to himself. He had a job to do; nothing would stand in his way.

Arthur quickly stripped off all his clothes, rolled them in a bundle and hid them under bushes. He took notebooks and pencils, stuffed them in his hat, then crammed the hat on his head. Shivering in the cold, he raced to the water's edge and plunged into the icy water. He made it safely to the other side, then lay panting for a while, trembling violently as the cold wind bit at his wet skin.

While resting, Arthur thought he heard a noise. With his poor eyesight, he peered about, but saw nothing. He hid behind some shrubs, watching silently, but still nothing happened. When at last he felt it was safe, he left his hiding place and searched for a path along the river bank. Soon, he had lost all sense of direction. Standing still for a moment, trying to find his bearings, he was startled by a loud shout near at hand.

"Milord! Milord English! Mister Evans!!"

Suddenly, a wet, wild-looking peasant, naked as Arthur himself, broke through the undergrowth. He grabbed Arthur's hands.

"Milord. Mister Evans. I follow you! This land very bad. Many Turks. I be your guide!"

Arthur was greatly relieved, and returned the pressure of his hands to the peasant. Together they climbed the steep river bank, then slid and stumbled down the other side toward the town of Ochievo. Quite unaware of any absurdity in their nakedness, they strode into the main street of the small town.

Arthur gasped! Most of the houses had been burned to the ground, the belongings of the inhabitants scattered in the streets. There was no sign of life. Arthur started taking notes, describing the horrible scene that met his gaze.

Suddenly, a warning hand on his arm stopped him.

"Milord Evans, *quick!*" The Bosnian drew him behind a wall. *"Turks!"* the Bosnian whispered with
fright. *"There, milord!"* He pointed down the street.

Clattering horses' hoofs in the distance warned them a
troop of cavalry was coming. They dashed into the
underbrush of the river bank for cover. They slid to
the water's edge, scraping shins and elbows, plunged in,
and swam across to safety.

As Arthur Evans's dispatches grew more detailed, his
friends at home began to worry. The things he described
could only be from a man who had seen with his own
eyes. He must be taking dreadful chances. Even a news-
paperman, they reasoned need not endanger himself as
Arthur appeared to be doing. It was almost a relief
when they learned an attack of fever had pinned him
down in Ragusa. They would have been less reassured
if they could have seen him!

Arthur did not look like a man recovering from fever.
He always loved the outdoors and his months of rough
living had other effects. He was tanned a rich bronze.
His eyes were clear and sparkling. His wispy moustache
had grown thick and strong. Indeed, with the right
clothes, Arthur could easily have been mistaken for a
Bosnian rebel chief.

The discomforts of the fever did not prevent him from
being up and about. It gave him a chance to do something he'd wanted to do for a long time. Arthur hired
fifteen men to help him, armed them with spades, then

set out to tackle the burial mounds he had seen long before.

On the plains of Canali, Arthur and his workmen
almost reached the center of the first mound. They
found nothing except a few bones, but Arthur's hopes
were high. Then, abruptly, news came that fighting
had now spread to Montenegro. Reluctantly, Arthur
abandoned his diggings.

This was not the first time, nor would it be the last,
that Arthur's archaeology was thrust to the back of his
mind. But the long grief of the living must come before
the mystery of the long dead. So Arthur believed; so he
acted.

No sooner had he arrived at a rebel strong point, than
a message came causing him to return to Ragusa immediately. Hastily, he turned over the food and med-
icines he'd brought.

Arthur ignored the dark and stormy night; on foot,
he set out at once through the strife torn countryside.

SIX

A "Spy" Goes to Jail!

DESTINY had an appointment with Arthur Evans in Ragusa. The message that had encouraged him to return, to travel dangerously all night, was from the friend of his correspondence, E.A. Freeman.

Mr. Freeman was important. He could help the relief fund. He was passing through Ragusa on his way to England and he did not wish to miss the opportunity to spend time with his young friend. So he sent the message, advising Arthur of his willingness to wait at Ragusa a few days.

Arthur and Freeman liked each other instantly. They shared a devoted passion for liberty. Both believed knowledge of the past held great value for the present. Not the least important, Arthur discovered, Mr. Freeman was traveling with his two daughters, Helen and Margaret.

Margaret Freeman had not enjoyed the trip through Italy with her father. She was not particularly interested in history, architecture, or the archaeology that was her father's life, and Ragusa bored her. However, as she began to understand more, her attitude changed. Mr. Freeman was usually so concerned with his work that all the daily needs of life were left to the girls. They did the ticket buying and arranged meals and lodgings.

If such a thing is possible, Arthur and Margaret Freeman "fell in love at first sight." So smitten was Arthur that, for a while, nothing else mattered.

Margaret was not beautiful, yet she had a captivating charm. Her petite figure was neat and well proportioned, and despite her strong and practical nature, she was extremely feminine. Thick, dark hair crowned her nicely shaped head. She blushed slightly, and felt her hands tremble as she greeted Arthur Evans. Arthur, who had had little thought for women until this moment, could hardly move his eyes from Margaret's face. To him, she was the most wonderful person he had ever met.

Gleeful as a schoolboy, Arthur decided to accompany the Freemans as far as Spalato (modern Split) on their homeward journey. And the romance between Arthur and Margaret blossomed. The few days at Spalato were sheer delight.

Arthur presented Margaret with a book which he inscribed to her. Margaret was now sure this dashing young man returned her feelings. They talked of his work and activity with the relief fund, and stole every moment they could to be alone.

All too soon, the few happy days came to an end.

"Will you write to me when I'm home?" Margaret asked.

Arthur assured her that he would, then bade them all a sad farewell. And letters began to pass between them frequently.

The embers of revolt continued to flare sporadically. When the rebels had arms and ammunition, they used them. When they did not, they hid in the mountains and things seemed quiet. The years passed slowly and there was a general apathy toward the perplexing situation. England herself had many problems to fight at home. There was the urgent problem of Home Rule for Ireland; the right to vote—for every man as well as for the privileged few—had yet to be won; and most dangerous of all, in the eyes of some, was the bitterly debated question of elementary (free) education for everybody. These issues, spawned by the inevitable growth of industrial wealth, were changing the way of life for Englishmen.

It was easy to forget Balkan troubles, but Arthur was not deceived by the apparent quiet. Thousands of refugees were still in great need. With Miss Irby, Arthur brought to them whatever succor he could gather from his countrymen. Austria had occupied Herzegovina and large parts of the troubled area. Slowly the Turks were being pushed back.

Eager to see Margaret and press his courtship, Arthur hurried to England. Soon after his arrival, he and Margaret announced their engagement and coming marriage.

It was wonderful to roam about Oxford and London with Margaret. Together, they visited the London exhibition of the treasures Schliemann had found at Troy. It was an inspiring experience, and Margaret began to comprehend the love her fiancé held for these ancient jewels. They were so lovely. For Arthur, there was much to puzzle over in the collection. A good deal of controversy raged about the age and historical place of Schliemann's treasure. Few were inclined to agree with his guesses about them. Arthur did not accept Schliemann's ideas but he felt very sure that the period from which these objects came was unknown. Apparently, what Schliemann had now found at Mycenae upheld this view.

Alas, the pleasures of London turned to sudden dismay for Margaret. In the midst of their happiness, Arthur had to go back to Ragusa.

"I *must* go, Margaret. There is money and relief we've collected which must get to Miss Irby. It's my work, and I am needed."

"But Arthur! Our wedding plans! How long will you be gone?"

Arthur consoled her, "I will soon be back. Also, because things seem quiet, do not be fooled as others are."

Margaret was only partly mollified. She began to learn how strong willed Arthur was. Once he decided on action, barring accident, nothing deterred him.

One of Arthur's sisters tried to explain, too. "Arthur has always come and gone as he pleased. You might as well get used to it. You should not misunderstand," she said. "He doesn't mean to be unkind or thoughtless. He's an idealist. When he takes up a cause, he must follow where his heart leads him."

John Evans and his wife Fanny, agreed. They felt the sooner Margaret realized the kind of man she was about to marry, the easier it would be for her. Margaret was marrying for better or worse, and she should understand that Arthur considered some things more important than his personal comfort and pleasure. Those who loved him had to live with this knowledge, as best they could.

"I should think," Fanny said to Margaret, "that he is much like your own father. Though he might seem inconsiderate at times, he loves you completely, and there has never been anyone else."

The warmth and affection Margaret received from Arthur's family comforted and sustained her during his absence. And she soon received letters from him which cleared her mind of any lingering doubts.

In his beloved Ragusa, Arthur felt he was "home." Flights of fancy in his new-found happiness with Margaret nourished the poet lurking in his soul and in his letters to her he sometimes let this show:

I love these eternal islands, these seas that should be valleys, and vales that should be seas. These hills on hills; monotonous, almost awful in their monotony, and yet how changeful! Blue today, tomorrow evanescent lilac, in the sunlight almost white;

or robed at dawn and setting in crimson and amethyst. Where else is Earth wedded like this in eternal sympathy to the heaven above? And this omnipresent inexorable rock: I love it, too, though sometimes I wonder at my love. I gaze on widening steppes, furrowed with strata lines of a most cruel demiurge: (a Greek name for the Creator) and yet it pleases me.

Arthur could not linger to watch the changing colors of the passing days. Poetry and archaeology were once more suppressed in the practical man of action. Looking ahead, Arthur sought a house, for he assumed that he and Margaret would live in Ragusa after they were married. The thought of asking Margaret if this would suit her did not occur to him.

In September, 1878, Arthur and Margaret were married. They stayed a while in Oxford, and when they were not visiting friends, Margaret busied herself sorting out the jumble of Arthur's papers and belongings, checking up on the chaotic condition of his finances. It was not long before she had them in order and a rather discouraging financial picture presented itself. In his papers, happily, she found tucked away a goodly sum of money which Arthur had completely forgotten. She believed that with her management they would get along well enough.

In October, they set out for Ragusa. When they arrived they discovered that the workmen had not finished the alterations on their house, so they moved into Arthur's old lodgings. Margaret grew thoroughly miserable. The roof leaked; there was no furniture. She appealed to Arthur's sister Alice, to come out and join

her, hoping Alice would help her get through this difficult time.   She was afraid she was going to be ill.   But
Arthur's parents would not let Alice go, since she was far
from strong herself.   And the rain continued to pour
from the skies in a never-ending torrent.

It was well for Margaret's peace of mind that this state
of affairs did not last too long.   By December, she was
able to move with Arthur into the new house, *Casa* San
Lazzaro.   Her spirits rose as she set about the task of
creating a home.   She was able, for a while, to forget the
aches and pains besetting her.

Early in January, 1879, Arthur set out to rejoin Miss
Irby and continue his work with the refugees.   When he
reached their headquarters at Knin, on the Dalmatian
coast of the Adriatic, he was astounded and heartsick at
what he found.   The Austrian authorities had driven
refugees back into Bosnia to occupy the homes and lands
that had been abandoned.   It was a very severe winter,
and many were dying of starvation.   This was not what
he expected from the Austrians.   No provision had been
made to help these unhappy people.   No crops had been
planted, so there had been no harvest.   And the protests
Arthur made brought no response.   It served only to
make the Austrians more suspicious of his activities.

When he returned home, Arthur's gloom lifted a
little.   He was happy to find Margaret lively and cheerful, fully recovered in spirits, and he permitted himself
to enjoy the peace and comfort of their charming new
home.   He settled down to work on the history of Illyria.

One sad fact had to be faced at this time. Margaret found herself unable to have children, but she and Arthur did not allow this to depress them. They both loved children and, having none of their own, found an orphan boy whom they fed, clothed, and sent to school.

When Arthur discovered the British consul at Ragusa was leaving, he thought he saw a good chance to assume the post. If he could get it, he would have added income, time to do his refugee work, and could still continue his writing and archaeological forays. His hopes for the consulship were high, for Gladstone again became Prime Minister in 1880.

With power in his hands, Gladstone proved himself more conservative and careful than he had appeared when opposing Disraeli. Much to Arthur's disgust, Gladstone did nothing about the sad things taking place in the Balkans. Arthur's published articles did not please the Austrians, and he realized that this combination of circumstances destroyed his hopes of being made consul.

So matters rested for a while. A great number of mysterious looking people continued to come and go at *Casa* San Lazzaro, as once they had visited Arthur at his lodgings. Rumors about Arthur were rife in Ragusa. Arthur Evans did help individuals who came to him for aid, but there was nothing mysterious about it. Margaret was doubtful and concerned by these odd visitors and said so.

"But, my dear woman, would you have me turn away

a man seeking what little I can give to feed his children?"

"Of course not, Arthur! But I feel very self-conscious when I go out. People look at me in a strange way which I cannot explain."

If Arthur was unaware that he was being watched by the Austrians, some of his friends were not, and they tried to warn him. He dismissed it as idle talk. He was doing nothing wrong and his dispatches to *The Guardian* could be read by anyone. There was no secret about where his feelings lay.

In May of 1880, a peculiar note was delivered to the *Casa* San Lazzarro.

"Look at this, Margaret," Arthur called. "It's written in Greek, I think! Where could it have come from?"

"What does it say?"

Arthur poured over the scrap of paper with the strange scribble. "It seems to be a message telling me that some 'spy' is in imminent danger of being arrested!"

Margaret's hands flew to her mouth. "I don't like it, Arthur. I don't like it one bit!"

"But my dear," he protested, "I don't know any spies! It's ridiculous. It must be some practical joke!"

Several months passed and nothing happened, and the disquieting incident was forgotten.

In the fall, Arthur, exhausted by his travels, fell sick. It was not a serious illness, and the enforced relaxation at least permitted him to do some writing. He still gave no credence to the belief that his name was being linked with all manner of mysterious plots, nor had he noticed the watch on his house. The old men and boys continued to make their visits to the house, often in the dark of night, and had they known the main reason for these visits, the Austrians could have saved themselves a lot of trouble.

Arthur Evans had stumbled upon a most fantastic tale, and he was following it through. He was fascinated by a story of ancient buried treasure. *If* the tale were true, and *if* he could get to the man who knew the whole secret, it would be the greatest discovery of ancient treasure ever made in the Balkans! One of Arthur's mysterious visitors had brought him a gold coin, and a fabulous story. While cutting stone for use on a new railway bed, two workmen had found a stone with an ancient inscription. When their companions left work for the day, these men returned to the scene of their labor. The Serbian and his Albanian friend dug beneath the inscribed stone. They found treasure! It was described to Arthur as a collection of gold coins and medals, all very old. A beautiful gold cross was the biggest piece of all. Unfortunately, when the Serbian and the Albanian were caught with the treasure by the other workmen, their companions killed them. Afterwards, the treasure was divided. Arthur's visitor promised to locate most of the pieces.

It was a likely story and, turning the gold coin over in his hands, Arthur decided to buy it. He wrote excitedly to his father of this event, and how he hoped to track down the rest of the treasure. He told his father he was close on the trail of the gold cross and hoped to buy it. If he could, it might prove very valuable in establishing some facts of early Serbian history.

After the first burst of excitement, Arthur began to have second thoughts. The more he examined the coin, the more suspicious he grew. Something was not right with it. Was it just a trifle too new to be an antique? Handling could, of course, have taken off some of the patina of age.

When next he saw the man who had told him this tale, Arthur questioned him closely. Finally, the man confessed. He and a friend, knowing Arthur's deep interest in these old coins, had faked the coins and made up the story of the ancient inscriptions and the murders to give authenticity to their tale. There was no gold cross. The coins were real gold, but they were clever fakes.

Arthur had been duped by forgers.

"That," he said to Margaret, "is what comes of being too eager. I got exactly what I deserved." It was a lesson he would remember.

The year 1881 gave way to 1882. Austria was reaping a bitter harvest in Herzegovina. Fighting was breaking out again. Every effort was being made to suppress the news, but Arthur kept getting his dispatches to England. Things were going badly for the Austrians and more and more they believed Arthur Evans a major cause of their troubles. He was openly discussed now, so much so, that a friend of Margaret's gave her a warning.

When Margaret told Arthur of this encounter, he was

not surprised. Even he realized, at last, the aura of suspicion that surrounded him. The British consul warned him, too. But he chose to stay in Ragusa. "After all," he told Margaret, "I have committed no crimes. What should I fear? Besides, my work must go on and I shall continue to send out the truth. I can't help it if the Austrians don't like it. I don't think they'll actually do anything except threaten me."

Arthur and Margaret were not left long in suspense. On March 7, 1882, a loud banging on the door of their house signaled the worst. Margaret drew back as a group of Austrian soldiers forced their way into the room.

"You're under arrest!" their captain said to Arthur. "We have proof that you are a rebel spy and that you are guilty of treason!" He motioned to two men. "Take him off!"

"This is ridiculous!" Arthur protested loudly.

The captain put out a detaining hand as Margaret started to follow her husband. "Not you! You stay here. And you are not to leave this house without permission!"

"Don't worry," Arthur called over his shoulder. "Get a message to the consul."

The captain grinned derisively, then brusquely ordered his men to search the house. Petrified, Margaret sank into a chair, watching the rough soldiers search the house. Every drawer, cupboard and room was thoroughly searched. When they finished, the soldiers had a table piled high with papers, which they carted off.

As soon as she was released, Margaret sent off frantic notes to the consul and to England, then hurried to the ancient prison of Ragusa. She was not allowed to see Arthur, although they let her send him food. Desperately anxious, she wrote again to John Evans, seeking advice and help.

Arthur Evans, the man who loved and fought hard for liberty, found himself locked in a small dark cell. His guards refused to let him have writing materials, nor would they let him have light. His captors feared he would use it to signal his rebel friends. There was nothing for him to do but sit and think.

At first, his great courage bore him up well. They might deny him writing materials, but that did not prevent him from smuggling out a message telling Margaret he was all right.

Margaret was shocked when the message came to her that night. "Why?" she cried to herself. "Aren't things bad enough? Why does he take such chances?" She, herself, was being closely watched, and she lacked Arthur's confidence and composure. She was convinced that if they thought it necessary, the Austrians would jail her, too! It was a relief when news reached her from London of the efforts being made for Arthur's release.

As the days lengthened into weeks, Arthur grew listless. Imprisonment, especially for a man of his temperament, was the hardest of things to bear. He sat, day after day, staring at the four bare walls of his cell. Finally, he was allowed to see Margaret. She was cheerful, feeling less alone, but Arthur was subdued, hardly responsive. Even news of his father's efforts for his release could not lift the deadening burden of imprisonment from his spirit.

The papers seized must have been a huge puzzle to the Austrians. There were masses of notes, including such perplexing things as detailed descriptions of mosques built on early Roman foundations. They even had Margaret's household account books. They found nothing to prove Arthur was a spy, but they tried hard to find in these papers secret codes and messages. They made sly remarks to Arthur that they had witnesses to testify to his spying. They spurred their efforts to build evidence against him. But, he was what he appeared to be, an archaeologist, historian, and a newspaper reporter.

The case brought an outburst in England. John Evans was a well-loved man with powerful friends. Some advised, "Let's make it a question for the House of Commons! That's bound to get some action." Others cautioned him against this. "It's better," they said, "to let diplomacy work quietly. If we openly try to force them to release him, we may only succeed in rousing their proud stubbornness. That will help no one."

John Evans went every day to the Foreign Office to seek news of his son. He found little comfort in their assurances that everything possible was being done. Wisely, he thought the diplomatic approach best, so he bore the suspense patiently.

Six weeks passed.

As abruptly as he had been seized, Arthur was released. Diplomacy had worked. It was mid-April when
he stumbled out of his dark and smelly cell. His deep
tan had faded to a yellowish pallor, and he looked ill.
His fine head drooped on his chest. But it was his spirit
that was damaged, not his physique.

Margaret, knowing what to expect, had already
shipped most of their things to England. It was an
enormous task, for Arthur had collected many antiquities. The furniture and draperies were all gone, too.
Casa San Lazzarro was empty. Margaret did not care;
she was glad to be going home.

Finding himself banished forever from any Austrian
territory or possession did not lift Arthur's spirits. They
were permitted but a few hours in which to leave the
place that had been home to Arthur for seven years.
Sadly, he looked about his beloved Ragusa as they left
it. It was dreadful to think he could never return. Miss
Irby had to carry on alone now.

Margaret chatted gaily in an attempt to cheer Arthur.
She, at least, had no regrets for what was left behind.

SEVEN

"Battles" at Oxford

THERE WAS great relief at Nash Mills, his father's house, when Arthur and Margaret reached England. Stories about the jail episode were rampant, and there were those who tried to make Arthur a hero. The family refused to have any part of such a thing. Their attitude was best summed up by one of Arthur's aunts, who remarked cryptically: "The boy has had a lesson which, I hope, will now make him stay at home!"

The talk annoyed and displeased Arthur, but he ignored it as much as possible. Gradually, his spirits improved, now the experience of isolation was behind him. He had other problems with which to cope. For one, banishment from Ragusa meant adjustment to English life. Color and romance and adventure were now seemingly lost to him. He could no longer sell eyewitness stories of the Balkans to his paper. And since payment had ended, he had to find something to do to augment his income.

Arthur was thirty-one years old when he and Margaret settled in the upper part of a house in Oxford. Once they were installed, with many of their bright furnishings from Ragusa to decorate the rooms, Arthur felt better. He tried to secure a post suited to his tastes and experience.

Arthur Evans now took the first steps on the road to his life's great work. And destiny once again took a hand in his affairs.

A position fell vacant at Oxford that seemed ideally suited to Arthur's tastes and ambitions. In this one job, if he could get it, his many interests could blend. The keeper of the Ashmolean Museum at Oxford retired in the year 1884. Arthur hoped to fill the vacant post.

The Ashmolean had once been an interesting place. It had come into being in 1677 when Elias Ashmole presented his collection of antiquities and rare objects to Oxford University. Later, he added his books and old manuscripts. Early in the nineteenth century, the Ashmolean enjoyed prominence because of what it had to offer students. Now it had fallen on times of neglect.

Arthur was astonished at what he discovered before applying for the post as its keeper. Many of the museum's treasures had been taken away. Its coins, manuscripts, and books had been moved to the Bodleian Library. (This official library of the university was

John Evans, c. 1855

Harriet Ann Dickinson,
wife of John Evans, c. 1857

A schoolboy
at Harrow, 1866

Arthur Evans with his wife, née Margaret Freeman, c. 1890

The excavations at Knossos, c. 1903

Above, left: rear view of restored North Entrance.
Right: portion of Grand Staircase at Knossos.

Arthur Evans
at Knossos, c. 1904

Reconstruction work showing varying levels and entrances to chambers

Minoan bronze figurine from Crete
showing acrobatic figure on bull.

Restored tapered columns at Palace of Minos;
note differing levels

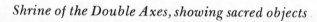

Large storage room with pits and jars

Shrine of the Double Axes, showing sacred objects

The figure-eight shields in "The Hall of Double Axes"

"The Ladies in Blue" fresco, restored by M. Guilleron

"The Cup Bearer" frescoes, West Entrance. Note reconstruction

"The Room of the Throne" with reconstructed frescoes

"The Horns of Consecration," believed originally to have surmounted South Side of Palace

Arthur Evans, 1928

named after Sir Thomas Bodley, who restored the building in 1602 after it had been destroyed by fire.) All that
remained in the Ashmolean were its archaeological material and a few dreary ethnological exhibits. Indeed,
the museum was so little used that one entire floor was
given over to students' examinations.

Arthur Evans was filled with excitement. Here was a
"battle" to his liking. In these "battles," all the varied
talents Arthur possessed came into focus and found their
purpose.

As he set about asking questions and checking information from various men of learning, Arthur grew in-
creasingly aware, almost gleefully so, that once again he
would be fighting for freedom, freedom of the mind.
The things he must win, and defend, in this new task
were very valuable.

Great schools are sometimes plagued with the petty
jealousies of small men in high positions. From his
student days, Arthur knew enough about Oxford to have
some idea of the problems facing him. Many educators
had allowed their minds to stultify, while they were in
solid administrative positions. Within their power lay
the means to crush this young upstart archaeologist,
should they so choose. Many of these men refused to
consider, despite a growing body of evidence, *any* European prehistory farther back than classic Greece, Egypt,
and the pharaohs. Arthur knew this was nonsense. Had
not his own father spent a lifetime gathering *evidence* of
man's incredibly ancient history?

The worst thing of all, Arthur believed, was for any man to allow his mind to become closed to new knowledge. Had not Heinrich Schliemann, strong in his faith, set the whole world of archaeology agog with his discoveries? These alone pushed civilization's age back beyond classic Greece!

At best, there was slight interest in the young science of archaeology at Oxford in 1884. There was not even a proper department to teach those students who were interested in the subject. For such a great university this was not right. Arthur knew how bitter would be the resentment of some of the powerful figures ranged against him, and the reason was simple. New information and proof would surely destroy the notions these men had believed all their lives.

Arthur weighed matters carefully, knowing he must move slowly. He studied his adversaries, if one could call them that, and planned his campaign.

Mr. Freeman once again proved himself a staunch ally of his son-in-law. He tried to warn Arthur. "They'll resist you," he said, "because they know full well your knowledge is greater than theirs." Mr. Freeman likened the task Arthur had set himself to the dark ages which followed the fall of Rome. "Then," he pointed out, "some wise men had fought the battle to get the study of ancient Greece admitted to scholarly circles. So you, now, must face such odds in setting the study of proper archaeology in its rightful place in the great schools of Oxford."

Oxford's schools were, indeed, great. In many instances they were great precisely because they produced rebellious sons who served their schools by refusing to be hidebound. Freeman agreed with Arthur that he should not shrink from the task. If the world is to learn and progress, all thinking men must encourage growth of understanding.

In June, 1884, Arthur Evans was appointed Honorable Keeper of the Ashmolean, as a "Home of archaeology in Oxford." The first small triumph was secured.

Arthur did not deliberately try to alienate those who opposed him. He understood their failure too well to be unkind. But forthrightly, he soon made plain that as Honorable Keeper, he would not tolerate the shabby treatment hitherto given the Ashmolean. One of his first tasks was to set forth, for his superiors at Oxford, his ideas of what his job meant—*and what he intended to do with it!*

Arthur Evans told them:

Our theme is History, the history of the rise and succession of human arts, institutions, and beliefs in our historic portion of the globe. The unwritten history of mankind precedes the written, the lore of monuments precedes the lore of books.

Consider for a moment the services rendered within quite recent years by what has been called pre-historic archaeology, but which in truth has never been more historic, in widening the horizon of our past. It has drawn aside the curtain, and revealed the dawn. It has dispelled, like the unsubstantial phantoms of a dream, those preconceived notions as to the origin of human arts and institutions at which Epicurus (340–270 B.C.) and Lucretius (97–53 B.C.) already laughed, before the days of biblical chronology.

It has taught us that, at a time when Britain formed still a part of the continent of Europe with arctic climate and another fauna; when the Thames was flowing into the Rhine, and the Rhine itself, perchance, was a tributary of 'that ancient river', the river Solent: when the very valley in which Oxford stands was only partly excavated, Man was already in existence here, fashioning his flint weapons to aid him in his struggle against the sabre-toothed tiger, or the woolly-haired rhinoceros. It has tracked him onwards to his cavern homes, and dragged into the light his bone harpoons, and the flint scrapers wherewith he cleaned in the grottoes of Dordogne the earliest known relics of other than the purest utilitarian art; it has followed him through the later periods of the Age of Stone in Europe, whetting and polishing his toma-hawks, or delicately flaking out his arrow heads and lance heads. It has dived to the lake bottoms, and reconstructed his pile (stilt) dwellings; it has fished out the very clothes he wore, the spindle whorls that spun their threads, the cereals that he learnt to culti-vate—nay, the very cakes he ate and the caraway and poppy seeds wherewith he flavoured them. It has shown us the beginnings of metallurgy, characterized in this quarter of the globe by the use of implements of bronze; and by the discovery of great pre-historic cemeteries, like that of Hallstadt in Upper Austria, it has revealed to us that at the close of this first Age of Metal, ancient lines of commerce were already bringing the Mediterranean shores into direct connection with the Baltic lands of fur and amber. We have as yet too little in our museum to illustrate these early chap-ters in the history of human arts.

In this statement of purposes, Arthur Evans indirectly paid tribute to his father and men like him. He knew how much the world owed to these men. Unaided by governments or foundations, often frowned upon by uni-versities, the enthusiasm and faith of these investigators from many countries revealed much of man's early history. Moved by sheer love of learning and discovery, and by belief in the importance of their work, they deserve the world's tribute for their selflessness.

Arthur continued his statement:

The science of archaeology has recovered some at least of the monuments that men deemed irrevocably lost. By patient collection of first hand materials, the pure gold of Hellenic workmanship has at last been cleaned and purged from its later alloy. We no longer see the image of the Hellenic genius darkly, as in a Roman mirror, but stand face to face with its undimmed glory. We have learnt, as we could not learn before, to distinguish the living form of the original from the polished grace of Imperial (Roman) copies and Renaissance restorations. Of Hellenic antiquities, as a whole, we have the tolerable nucleus of a collection: but ... in its present state our collection is unworthy of a great university. Whole classes of objects, and those not the least important, are almost entirely unrepresented.

He complained to his audience of the lack of Greek vases and objects of Greek art in the Ashmolean, and showed them some of his own collection of these things to prove his point. He concluded:

It is absolutely necessary for us to have a small annual sum to spend on the development of our collections. It does not become a great university like ours to depend on charity alone for the promotion of objects inseparably connected with its central studies. Those who regard the Museum in which we are now assembled as a mere repository of curiosities may rest content with the accident of benefaction. Those, and they are, I am convinced, an increasing number, who look to the Ashmolean as a future home for archaeological research and teaching, will require something more.

Browsing through the rooms of the Ashmolean, Arthur usually carried a late seventeenth century catalogue in his hands. He was able to identify objects from the original endowments when he retrieved them from odd corners into which they had been stacked. There were many things that were simply curiosities; others held great value, such as prehistoric bronze weapons from ancient Britain, and tomahawks brought from early Virginia. These items were rare. Many like objects were rescued from obscurity.

Arthur studied the layout of the buildings, and made plans for heating them properly.

Arthur's "small annual sum" was small only in his eyes. To accomplish his aim, considerable money would be needed. Happily, his views, shared by many others, eventually prevailed.

Of course, Arthur had nothing against high-principled men and women who cheerfully gave endowments and collections to museums. He welcomed such gifts, but it was many years before the great schools worked, themselves, to build their stores of antique treasures and enrich the standards of learning.

Early in his keepership, Arthur met a man whose help and support proved invaluable. Mr. C.D.E. Fortnum, a wealthy man, believed he had found in Arthur Evans a man much to his liking. Fortnum had a marvelous collection of fine art, and he was anxious to give this collection to Oxford University. He also offered a large sum of money, over three hundred thousand dollars, for its upkeep. He also insisted on certain conditions for its maintenance. But nothing had been settled. Arthur Evans and Fortnum developed a healthy respect for one another in the many discussions about the proposed gift.

When he had this gift to tempt those who disbursed university funds, Arthur's plans were taken more seriously. With this financial backing, he faced the years of bickering school politics and personality clashes with those who opposed the Ashmolean. Slowly he made his way forward, pressuring wherever he could to gain his objective.

Arthur ousted those who were using the Ashmolean as an examination hall. He installed new display cases, made rapid progress in classifying and cataloguing the museum's treasures. He soon found that his assistant, Mr. C.F. Bell, was wholly reliable, capable, and a faithful supporter. This freed Arthur from much routine work, and he could travel, to search for new things to add to the growing collection under his care.

Moving about the ancient sites of Greece, Arthur was amazed. The incredible treasures found at Mycenae, Tiryns, and Troy, gripped his imagination. The clay pottery, figurines, gold death masks, necklaces, gold and silver cups, bronze pots of all kinds, were different from anything found before. The people who made and used these objects—where did they come from? Were they preclassic Greeks who lived long before the rise of Hellenic Greece?

The gold beads and jewels, the clay and metal seals,

indicated a type of dress and customs hitherto unknown. Peering nearsightedly at them, he became convinced that the signs inscribed were some kind of writing symbols. Alas that there were so few of the seals available. And if it *was* writing, what could it possibly say?

In Egypt, Arthur knew, there were paintings in tombs and temples, some of which pictured a strange people bearing gifts to pharaoh. These painted figures were not Egyptians, nor were they black-skinned people from the south. The Egyptians simply called them the Keftui, people from the great green sea. But who were they? Where were they from? They were certainly not Greeks! It was a complex and tangled puzzle.

As he gazed out across the blue Mediterranean Sea, Arthur pondered. And the soft echo of a mysterious island tapped lightly at his ear. Heinrich Schliemann had believed the island of Crete held a great prize for the archaeologist who would venture to dig there, and Arthur was inclined to agree with him. But opposition from the Turks, and death, had robbed Schliemann of the chance to excavate in Crete, and Arthur had to return to his museum with the treasure he'd acquired.

The early years of the 1890s dealt Arthur a bewildering series of tragic blows and comforting triumphs. It was a blessing for him that he so loved his work, for he was able to retreat into it from the sadness that came to him.

In the fall of 1890, Fanny Phelps grew seriously ill.

John Evans was distraught, for it soon became obvious that Fanny could not live. Margaret felt it more keenly than almost any other member of the family, for Fanny had been a second mother to her. While Fanny lingered, Arthur's father managed to pull together his courage to face the worst. Yet, when his wife died near the end of September, he felt he could never recover from his loss. Lonely, he tried to concentrate on his coins, and his business.

Arthur Evans was now well established at Oxford, and he began to look for a site to build a home. He found a place he liked at Boar's Hill, a place he had loved to roam while a student. The quiet and lush woods appealed to him. In his mind's eye he envisioned the house he could build there. He thought he could alter the landscape, recreate it to resemble the countryside around Ragusa.

When he first discussed with his father purchasing the sixty acres of land, John Evans was not much impressed. It seemed extravagant. But John Evans did not offer strenuous objections. He had to foot the bills for his son's plans, but he allowed Arthur to proceed with prices and estimates for building.

The Ashmolean was growing fast and needed more room. Arthur had a huge collection of his own by now. Perhaps in some way, he thought, the new house could be joined with the museum. It would all be so very convenient. During his travels to Greece and Crete he had acquired for himself many seals with strange inscriptions. Sometimes it proved expensive to buy them from the villagers, but he was persistent. Now, much of his spare time was spent copying the marks on paper, trying to decipher and find meaning in them.

The year 1892 continued the pattern of mixed blessings and sad tragedies. John Evans met a highly intelligent younger woman with whom he had a good deal in common. Maria Lathbury, whose father was a friend of John Evans, was a handsome lady, and she had a great regard for John.

The whole family welcomed Maria, delighted with John's choice. Their pleasure was even greater when John was summoned before Queen Victoria in 1892. He emerged from the audience with his Queen with overflowing heart, *Sir John Evans,* Knight Commander of the Bath. It was a very high honor indeed, but richly deserved.

Arthur's father had traveled a long way from the poor disappointed lad who had set out to work in his uncle's mills; the Queen had honored him as a great man of science and learning.

In June of the same year, 1892, John and Maria were married.

EIGHT

A Phoenix Rises

HAPPINESS for his father's successes did not eliminate the misfortunes which continued to badger Arthur. His beloved Margaret began to ail; he still had to fight niggardly school budgets for enough money to carry out his plans for the Ashmolean Museum; and when work began on the new house, Youlbury, at Boar's Hill, expenses ran many times higher than the estimates.

As if to confound the difficulties, Margaret's father died. Old friends and loved ones were rapidly disappearing about Arthur and Margaret; the world was changing, becoming a fast moving, bewildering place—none of this helped Margaret's condition.

Worried about his wife's health, Arthur made a suggestion. "Margaret, why don't we go abroad for a while? I have to make a trip to Greece anyhow. After this long, gloomy winter, a change of scene and some sunshine will do you good."

Margaret looked at her husband skeptically. She was not at all sure she felt up to traveling. True enough, it was much easier than it had once been to get about on the Continent. "I don't know, Arthur," she said, rather apathetically. "You might be right. It would be nice to visit with my sister Helen for a while."

"Good," Arthur said. "Then it's settled. Also, you remember, I must go down to Sicily. I've got to check those few details for your father's last book. Then it should be ready for the publisher."

Leisurely, Arthur and Margaret journeyed to Europe and made their way to Bordighera, where Helen was staying in Italy. Margaret grew worse.

"I don't feel like going on, Arthur," Margaret admitted. "I shall stay with Helen and rest. You go on and I'll meet you at Alassio on your way back."

Dubiously, Arthur asked, "Are you sure you'll be all right here?"

"Of course I shall be," Margaret assured him. "A little rest will strengthen me." Margaret's grief for her father persisted, and she seemed strangely unable to shake off her sorrow.

Arthur went on to Athens. He talked to several scholars who were doing archaeological work in Greece, and he poked about in the ruins of the Acropolis, finding bits of broken pottery he thought pre-Mycenaean. Nobody else seemed to think it important. He spent some time studying the seal rings from Mycenae and listened to lectures by men who had worked with Schliemann.

And the echo from the mysterious island across the sea tapped a little louder at his ear; but still he did not hear.

For the Ashmolean, Arthur found a broken sword from Mycenae, which he felt could be restored. A lovely gold Mycenaean bead he found among "a lot of rubbish." He acquired some figurines from Thebes which seemed to show stages of development from prehistoric to classic Greek art. Altogether, February was a pleasant month.

With his treasures safely on their way to England, Arthur rejoined his wife at Alassio. He was glad to find that she was not worse, though she seemed little better. Eagerly, he talked to Margaret about the things he found and bought for the Ashmolean.

"You know, Margaret," he said. "I'm becoming convinced that Heinrich Schliemann barely lifted the curtain of a great mystery. It's a pity he died so suddenly a couple of years ago. He seemed to think there was something to be found in Crete. And he may well have been right! Perhaps, one of these days, I'll go and have a look. I ought to be able to find some more inscribed beads or seals at least. I wouldn't be surprised to find nearly every peasant wearing one as a luck charm."

While they were preparing to journey back to England, on March 11, 1892, Margaret suddenly collapsed in great pain. Anxiously, Arthur tried to soothe and comfort her, but suddenly, within an hour, still grasping her husband's hand tightly, she died.

Blind with grief, Arthur Evans faced the unhappy ordeal of arranging his wife's funeral. He poured out his sorrow in a letter to his father:

I cannot yet fully realize the greatness of the blow which has fallen upon me. I do not think anyone can ever know what Margaret has been to me. All seems very dark and without consolation.

A few days later, he wrote home again:

I try to call up her brave spirit, but one must have time to recover strength. I am thankful that all is over that had to be done. The funeral took place on Sunday after afternoon service, in the English corner of the cemetery. I made her a wreath of marguerites and scented broom and white Mediterranean heath. She had often gathered nosegays of it when we walked about the hills here together last year.

Arthur Evans's tribute to his dead wife is engraved on her tombstone at Alassio:

To her father, she had once been as a right hand: to her husband—in wild travel, through troublous times, and in quiet study—she was a helpmate such as few have known. Her bright energetic spirit, undaunted by suffering to the last, and ever working for the welfare of those around her, made a short life long.

Though only forty-two years old, Arthur had seen death snatch from him the women he loved. First, his unforgettable mother, and then the ever helpful and loving Fanny Phelps. Now, his grief for Margaret made his heart like lead. All did, indeed, "seem dark and without consolation."

But Arthur Evans was to rise, phoenixlike, from the ashes of his grief. He would love again, and he would have a love that was wife, mother, sister, sweetheart, life itself—but not in the form of a woman. A love lay buried on a mysterious island across the blue sea. He had not responded, yet; but the call of this love grew ever more insistent.

As the sad days and weeks dragged along, Arthur Evans buried his grief in his work, and slowly discovered a store of courage he did not know he possessed. Calmly, now, he continued to build the house Margaret never saw. Gradually, he reconstructed his devastated life. And in June, 1893, came an event which made him observe, "I must say, I think it is all very strange."

His father, now quite elderly, and Maria, presented him with a baby half sister.

By 1894, ten years and six months after he had taken the post of keeper, Arthur Evans had transformed the Ashmolean. With the help of Fortnum, and willing men of the university, he had turned the dilapidated museum into a vital center of teaching and learning. A whole new wing had been added, making room for the growing collection of archaeological wonders. One of Arthur's greatest joys was the knowledge that the university now had a Department of Classical Archaeology, and it was housed in the new Ashmolean.

During the long years of this accomplishment, Arthur was not idle in other directions. He continued numismatic research (the study of coins and medals) which remained a constant source of interest, and he gave special attention to British iron-age antiquities. He published many articles on this subject with his conclusions, and also published two papers on coins found in Sicily, and medallions from Syracuse.

In 1894, Arthur traveled to the valley of the kings in Egypt. In the same year, he published the results of an archaeological expedition made years before—the Roman villa at Frilford, in England. And his thoughts turned more and more toward the island of Crete.

During the next few years, Arthur made sporadic excursions to Crete. He found many more inscribed "charms" and seals which convinced him still more that this island possessed hidden secrets of enormous importance. He inquired into the price of some land he considered excavating, but old political troubles smouldered. Greeks and Turks still struggled for control of Crete. The difficulties proved too much. Yet the notion that this island held great secrets was firmly fixed in his mind, and a mound which had interested Schliemann now captured Arthur's imagination.

Arthur began to formulate theories of pre-Hellenic times. Some of these ideas he published in 1894, a study of *Primitive Pictographs and a prae-Phoenician Script from Crete and the Peloponnese.*

Excerpts from his diary of this same year show the growing excitement he began to feel:

March 15, 1894:   Able to visit bazaar: found a man from whom I bought 22 early Cretan stones, some coins, one of silver and of Phaestos (Crete) and a small marble image from Phaestos....

March 16, 1894:

Visited Jean G. Misotakis, *Vice Consul de*

Russie à Candia. (Russian vice consul at Candia, modern Iraklion) He has a whole collection of things from Cave of Idean Zeus . . . secured 21 gem stones and Mycenaean ring from Knossos. . . .

March 17, 1894: In the evening some excitement. Knowing the straight road, I walked back at 9:45 in clear moonlight from the chief café to the inn. Hardly in my room, than three Christians burst into the inn to say that two Turks had followed me to assassinate me, and would have stabbed me if they had not come after them. I know nothing of this; the road seemed quite solitary. People seem excited about it, but what is certain is that I was not. . . .

Studying the mound Schliemann had once tried to buy, Arthur Evans believed it well worth archaeological attention. It seemed to him that the mound was artificially created. A few traces of man-worked stone lay about. Did its present height simply represent the build up of the debris of ages, making the site look like a hill? And as the years passed, he became eager to acquire the property.

By 1900, the Turks had finally left Crete, and Arthur at last succeeded in buying the site of the mound he so earnestly desired.

NINE

The Clay Tablets

THE ISLAND OF CRETE lies southeast of the Greek mainland, in the Mediterranean. It is an archaeologist's paradise. When Arthur Evans began his work on the island,
it was hardly touched by the spades of diggers into the
past. Whatever his intuition may have told him, Arthur
could not have known that what he started would become one of the wonders of the twentieth century!

Greek lore is full of tales about this strange island—
most so fantastic they had long been considered myths.
Homer's *Odyssey* is a saga of gods, goddesses, heroes and
heroines who, if they ever existed, had left little or nothing behind them to prove it. Yet, as Schliemann had
shown, Homer was far more than an imaginative poet.
At their cost, many archaeologists ignored Homer's
geography, his historical truth, however farfetched it
seemed; yet Homer had more than once been proven
a reliable guide to the past.

Arthur knew that book nineteen of the *Odyssey* described a Crete which must have been great centuries before classic Greece was born.   If this story held any truth, then it could be conjectured that after prehistoric Crete's fall from power, a dark age had descended upon the Mediterranean world, a dark age that could compare with the one that followed the fall of Rome.   Therefore, Arthur wondered, did it follow that prehistoric Crete knew a culture and civilization as great as later Greece? He decided to follow Schliemann's footsteps.

Book nineteen of the *Odyssey,* dealing with the fantastic adventures of Ulysses, describes Crete in its greatness:

> Crete awes the circling waves, a fruitful soil!
> And ninety cities crown the sea-born isle:
> Mix'd with her genuine sons, adopted names
> In various tongues avow their various claims:
> Cydonians, dreadful with bended yew,
> And bold Pelgasi boast a native's due:
> The Dorians, plumed amid the files of war,
> Her foodful glebe with fierce Acheans share:
> Cnossos, her capital of high command;
> Where sceptered Minos with impartial hand
> Divided right; each ninth revolving year,
> By Jove received in council to confer.
> His son Deucalion bore successive sway; ...

Examination of the passage, though there are many different versions, gave Arthur an astonishing picture. *If* Knossos had ever existed, it must have been a highly cosmopolitan city, housing people of many races.   They enjoyed full rights and privileges under the laws of great

Minos. "Cydonians, dreadful with bended yew." Were these, perhaps, with their deadly bows and arrows, the king's bodyguard? Certainly in Homer's brief description, their very name struck terror in other hearts.

Dorians and Acheans, fierce and warlike—were these the people who destroyed glorious Troy before, in their turn, forging Greek civilization? Deucalion? Arthur wondered if this could mean a son of Minos who followed his father to power.

One fabulous tale of ancient Crete deals with the first recorded dream of human flight. In this legend, which had varying versions, Minos had a very clever and skillful architect, Daedalus. Daedalus was like a prehistoric Leonardo da Vinci, he had so wide a range of interests and talents.

Minos desired Daedalus to construct a labyrinth. In this labyrinth, Minos kept a monstrous creature, half bull, half man, the Minotaur. The Minotaur was worshipped as a god. Regular sacrifice of seven maidens and seven youths was made to the beast.

Minos sent his son Androgeus to compete in the games at Athens, according to the legend. Androgeus won his contests, and he was murdered by Aegeus, who was blindly jealous of his competitor. In reprisal for the murder of his son, Minos sacked Athens, and exacted an annual tribute of the seven finest youths and seven fairest maidens for sacrifice to the Minotaur.

When the labyrinth was completed, Minos quarreled with Daedalus. Perhaps the king feared his architect would reveal the secret of the labyrinth? Minos threw

Daedalus and his son Icarus, into prison. While he languished in prison, Daedalus had a marvelous idea. He made a framework of wings to which he fixed masses of feathers with wax. Warning his son not to fly too near the sun, they escaped from the prison.

Alas, Icarus was entranced with the sensation of flight. He forgot his father's warning. Flying higher and higher, the hot sun melted the wax on his wings. The wings collapsed and Icarus was dashed to the earth and killed. Sorrowing, Daedalus flew on his way and is supposed to have escaped to Sicily.

These myths and legends raced about in Arthur's mind for he knew that generally, in such folk tales, there is some germ of truth.

Another incredible tale of Daedalus lived on. Minos, greatly concerned by the need to defend and guard his broken coastline, gave the problem to Daedalus. The answer Daedalus found was astonishing. He constructed a bronze mechanical man—surely the first robot in all history! Talos, the bronze monster, was supposed to patrol the coast three times a day. As he moved, great tongues of fire issued from his mouth, putting fear into all who beheld the awesome sight. A silver coin, reputedly dating from the fourth century B.C., found in Crete, shows Talos as a young man, busy hurling stones at the enemies of Minos as he strides his patrol.

One more legend, which Arthur could not ignore, and which had important bearing on later discoveries at Crete, concerns the Greek hero Theseus. Growing weary of the continued tribute of youths and maidens,

Theseus begged his father, Aegeus, for permission to accompany the next tribute ship to Knossos. He vowed
to slay the terrible Minotaur. Reluctantly, Aegeus
agreed. It was arranged that if Theseus succeeded, his
ship was to carry white sails when he came home. If he
failed, the sails were to be black.

Theseus, at Knossos, met Ariadne, daughter of Minos,
and she immediately fell in love with him. On learning
Theseus's mission, Ariadne agreed to help. She placed
a ball of wool or thread, and a sword in the hands of her
lover. She gave one end of the strand to Theseus who
then made his way into the dreaded labyrinth, unwind-
ing the strand as he progressed. To find his way back
out again, all he needed to do was follow the strand back
to Ariadne.

(In the museum at Candia, Crete, there is a very strange clay
object. This object, about eight inches long, has come to be called
Ariadne's Clew Box. Nobody knows what its purpose was.
Vaguely, it resembles a modern piggy bank. Where the pig's
snout would be, there is a protrusion and beneath this a slit like
a mouth. At one side there is a small round hole. Two legs are
at the front, again looking like crude pig's feet. There is no
proof that this object ever belonged to Ariadne. Some people
have speculated that this strange object held the ball of thread, or
string, when Theseus entered the labyrinth. Perhaps, though, it
might have been a Minoan piggy bank! Coins could have passed
through the "mouth" below the snout. The hole at the side may
only have been for a thrifty Cretan to check his savings!)

Arthur Evans had long been familiar with all these
ancient legends, but unlike his predecessor Schliemann,
he refrained from jumping to conclusions, or postulating

wild theories. He was a more sound and steady archaeologist. But he felt sure of the importance of Crete.

At one time, according to the ancient historians, Crete
had been well wooded with giant trees. If this were so,
the island had changed beyond recognition. The soil
still produces fine olive trees, but nothing matches the
early descriptions. The climate is harsh in winter, hot,
dusty, and uncomfortable in summer. Of Homer's
ninety cities, there was little trace. But archaeologists,
if they are not to be misled, must make due allowances
for time's changes.

The island looked pleasant enough to Arthur when
he gazed upon it. Soft, silvery green olive trees dotted
the landscape in groves, sloping gently toward the east-
west mountain range. The highest peak, Mount Ida,
has a snow-capped tip that has been tied in with Greek
and earlier legends for thousands of years. The great
Zeus is supposed to have been born in a cave on this
mountain. Arthur, after his several visits, had grown
to love the island and its people.

At first, Arthur was not really looking for much more
than additional examples of the beads and seals which
bore the strange inscriptions he found so engrossing to
study. Always a shy, retiring man, Arthur had become
more so since the loss of Margaret. At forty-nine years
of age, his small frame seemed to have shrunk a little.
He was a bit more stooped at the shoulders, the result
of a lifetime of peering from his nearsighted eyes. He
could be lively and jolly, as enthusiastic as a schoolboy.

"Prodger" still sailed around his head when he got excited, but he shunned the glaring light of personal publicity. The ideals which had governed his life still burned strong and bright in his soul.

In insisting on hiring a band of mixed workers right from the start, Arthur hoped to demonstrate that Christians and Moslems *could* cooperate, *could* work together in harmony, side by side. Indeed, if they were to build upon their new state of freedom, they *must* work together. And under his benevolent charge they did!

On March 23, 1900, work began. Almost with the first spade that was thrust into the earth, Arthur Evans shot back ten thousand years in time, according to his own reckoning. And with the first spadeful of earth, he showed himself to be one of the greatest archaeologists of all time. When he became aware of the immensity of the earth's rich yield, he gathered about him a skilled team. With the passing years, this team changed frequently. Always, however, there were men of special knowledge in geology, art, architecture, experts of many kinds at work on the site. Arthur enjoyed the eager assistance of Duncan Mackenzie, an already experienced archaeologist, and Theodore Fyfe, among many others. Their knowledge of construction techniques helped Arthur Evans avoid many pitfalls that might otherwise have led him astray in his digging. Later, J.D.S. Pendlebury, another trained archaeologist, assisted closely in the work for many years. Some of the most magnificent restorations were handled by the artist, M. Guilleron.

Arthur had with him on this first expedition, Mr. Mackenzie and the engineer-architect, Theodore Fyfe. Mackenzie did a very fine job of keeping records. Each object was carefully recorded for position, depth or condition and classification.

The carbon 14 process of dating antiquities still lay half a century in the future. Carbon 14, the radioactive atom of the element carbon, is absorbed by every living thing. But when something dies, the intake of carbon 14 stops. Disintegration slowly sets in—half the carbon 14 is lost every 5,500 years—and thus, with the use of a geiger counter, the loss of carbon can be measured and the age of an object determined to within two hundred years. Arthur Evans did not have any such advanced method at his disposal. But he did have a vast knowledge of prehistory. With characteristic steadiness and quiet care, he relied upon the aid of geological evidence, stratification, for approximating age.

A series of test pits were dug at different places on the site. Sometimes they were as deep as 26 feet or more. The layers of earth in these pits can be read like a book by trained geologists. Geology is an exciting science. By examining the different strata of the earth, much can be told about how the layers were formed, why they vary from one another, and what natural and man-made events accounted for changes. Arthur Evans had much sound knowledge of geology and as his work progressed he often found it necessary to consult other experts for their views on his findings.

The test pits revealed an astounding story. They showed immediately that Arthur was right. The mound *was* artificial. Their task, in a sense, rather than digging *into* the earth, was more a matter of peeling back layers built up by men for thousands of years. The pits led Arthur to believe that the site of Knossos, capital of Minos, had been continually occupied for at least ten thousand years! (Some archaeologists prefer to halve that figure, but the whole story has yet to be told.)

The top layers of the pits, at a few feet below the surface, yielded objects of a high and brilliant workmanship. Going on down the pit, other layers gave up pottery and utensils belonging to earlier periods. This told the eager archaeologists that Knossos had known more than one period of greatness. It also revealed a mystery. These people were completely unknown except through ancient Greek legend. How could they have so completely disappeared from history?

The very crude objects and debris, found at the bottom of the pits, told Arthur a tale of neolithic occupation of the site of Knossos. With this material he was very familiar. Just how deep the layer of neolithic relics went, nobody could guess.

In his knowledge of prehistory, Arthur found other clues to help him. Some of the pottery and tools and weapons, he recognized instantly. Their like could be seen painted on the walls of tombs and temples in Egypt! These people, then, could be the Keftui! Since the ancient Egyptians left many dates and records, by matching the pottery found at Knossos with that on temple walls, an approximate date for its use in Crete could be found.

"This is truly astonishing," Arthur said excitedly to Mackenzie. "We can actually place some of these things precisely in the proper periods, thousands of years back. It's unbelievable!"

Arthur thought, from what the test pits had revealed, he would need at least a year to gather the material, analyze its meaning, and complete the story. *Forty years later, he was still hard at work!*

Knowing the site of Knossos to be worth excavation, Arthur progressed rapidly. Close to the surface of the ground, as layers of earth were peeled away, walls appeared. Basketful after basketful of earth was removed. Each basket was carefully sifted several times for gold beads, seals, rings, and other small objects that could easily be lost. Care also had to be taken against pilfering.

As the level of the earth was lowered, the walls rose. Soon it could be seen that Arthur was excavating an immensely complex building. The twists and turns were, indeed, labyrinthine.

"This must be it!" gasped Arthur. He stood looking at the result of the day's work. "Shades of Daedalus! *This must be the palace of Minos!*"

Fragments of frescoes, once painted on plaster in glowing colors, came to light. It would take time and tremendous effort to put them together again. Reverently, the pieces were lifted from the hiding places of centuries. Each piece was carefully cleaned, its position

noted, the room it came from. Each room, as it was revealed and cleaned of debris, was given a name or a
number for easy reference. Later, Arthur could analyze,
and from these clues he might learn the purposes of the
rooms from the objects found in them. Already, decorations of the painted fragments, casual examination of the
bits of heads, arms, and legs, assured Arthur he had
found an unknown civilization!

Small groups of cups were dug up, and more fragments of frescoes. Bits of frescoes, some large, others
quite small, could be matched. There could be no
doubt. Back into the world came the Keftui! These
were "the people of the great green sea."

This, then, was the fabled Minoan civilization. A
myth, garbled and distorted through thousands of years
was revealing its germs of truth. This city of Knossos,
capital of Minos—for it must be a city—had existed and
flourished hundreds of years before the rise of Greece.

"Look at the details of the costumes," Arthur said,
pointing to some of the fragments. "I've never seen anything like them."

The archaeologists pressed on. There was so much to
be done. Earth was slowly cleared from what seemed to
be a terrace. Among the debris, the tops of immense
jars, bigger by far than the height of a man, began to appear. Obviously they were standing on the floor of this
terrace. These great jars found *in situ* (in their original
position) brought intense excitement. The workmen
had reached a part of the palace storage area. Great

quantities of oil and wine and grains had evidently been kept in these huge jars. Minos must have been very wealthy. Perhaps soon, Arthur hoped, they would be able to form a clear idea of the layout of the whole building.

This excitement paled almost to insignificance by what immediately followed.

On the last day of March, 1900, a mere seven fabulous days since work began, the spades uncovered a cache of clay tablets, each about three inches long and half as wide! Arthur's emotion was almost more than he could bear. With beating heart, a silent prayer of thanks on his lips, Arthur gently held the tablets in his hands. He saw at once that the tablets were inscribed in a form of linear script. So this ancient civilization *did* have a highly developed writing! He noted a marked resemblance to the inscriptions he'd studied on seals found at Mycenae and other places on the mainland of Greece. He could scarcely wait to examine them closely and compare the markings. The search for specimens of this strange script had originally brought him to Crete, so these small clay tablets were a prize beyond his wildest dreams.

Discoveries came so fast, that Arthur had to increase his work force to a hundred men. More walls were uncovered, and in some places they found marks, in the linear script, of the masons who had built the walls. More fragments of frescoes appeared, elaborately painted and designed. These were treated the same way as the earlier finds. Some of the pieces now being found were quite large.

Easter holidays, and a dust-stirring wind, retarded work for a while, but by April 5, Arthur and his men were again hard at work. And on this day was discovered parts of a fresco picturing a human figure that is, perhaps, the most famous and wonderful of all the frescoes at Knossos. Only fragments from the shoulders to the navel were found to be there when the pieces were put together. At first, it was thought to be the figure of a woman. This was, no doubt, due to the amazingly slim waist and fantastic costume of the figure. Later study, and other frescoes, proved it to be the figure of a man. M. Guilleron, using his imagination, combined with details observed in other frescoes, reconstructed the figure. He is known today, and has been wonderfully restored, as "The Cupbearer." He is a life-sized figure, and physically quite different from ancient Egyptians and Greeks. There is a flow and movement in his figure quite unlike the stilted Egyptian forms shown in paintings and statues. This quality of "life" in art was carried to a high standard by the later Greeks.

(M. Guilleron's many restorations of frescoes are sometimes questioned for accuracy and are referred to by some people as "Guilleron-Minoan.")

For Arthur, a small portion of the story of the Minoan people already began to emerge from the many clues. "The Cupbearer" had reddish skin. Perhaps this meant only that he had liked to tan his skin in the sun? Maybe it meant only that Minoans liked the color? Apparently they seldom had need for much clothing, since his costume, though finely cut and sewn, was very scant. The mode of dress, far from appearing ancient, was so outlandish the Minoans might be taken for some futuristic people in a science-fiction story. "The Cupbearer's" profile showed a straight nose, full lips, dark lustrous eyes, and an altogether noble countenance. He wore a necklace, ear ornaments, and a bracelet. He carried a narrow-necked cup in a gesture of offering to the gods. The very small waist was circled by a thick rolled band of metal or leather, from which a dainty loincloth was suspended.

Charred columns, calcined debris, and marks of fire on walls, gave Arthur pause. Another mystery to be grappled with later. He felt sure that fire had played a big part in the final destruction of the Palace of Minos.

The work continued laboriously. Important fragments of the frescoes were carefully covered around the edges and on the back with plaster to give them a firm base; they could then be moved to a safe place for later study, and piecing together.

The news of Arthur's quick success at Knossos created a sensation. His father was delighted and sent funds to help with the work. News of the discoveries brought other archaeologists to Crete, from all countries. Such a bewildering array of objects were being found, the problem of relating and classifying became extremely difficult.

The complex of buildings, even at this preliminary stage, already spread over two acres of ground! Surely, Arthur surmised, this must have been a powerful and strong Minos, and his people had prospered mightily.

More and more clay tablets were uncovered, some with pictographs of horses and chariots along with linear signs. Arthur wondered to himself: "Can the strange marks be words? Can they be read? If it proves possible to decipher them . . ." the thought was overpowering, "the Minoans may speak to me from their past, from thousands of years B.C.!"

TEN

"A Puzzle Wrapped in a Mystery"

WHEN THE SEASON's digging drew to a close, Arthur had accumulated a puzzling mass of artifacts. These had to be sorted, classified, and catalogued, and Arthur planned to restore as many as possible.

He realized that here, indeed, was a mystery. As he examined whole and broken pots, beads, seals, necklaces, and jewels, figurines and clay tablets, the need for a system became acute. All this material had to be organized, then presented to the world of scholars for study and comment so that they could assist in solving the mysteries.

The different geological strata made it abundantly clear to Arthur that Knossos had enjoyed several flowerings. The objects from the different levels of the pits

MINOAN PERIODS

Approximate dates		
	3200 B.C.	
		NEOLITHIC
	2700 B.C.	
I	2700 B.C.	
II	2400 B.C.	EARLY MINOAN
III	2100 B.C.	
I	2100 B.C.	
II	2000 B.C.	
		MIDDLE MINOAN (Age of palaces)
III	1775 B.C.	
	1600 B.C.	
I	1600 B.C.	
II	1450 B.C.	
III	1400 B.C.	LATE MINOAN
	1200 B.C.	
	1100 B.C.	Decline

EGYPTIAN DYNASTIES

I, II	**Founded by MENES**
III	**ZOSER**
IV	**CHEOPS (KHUFU)** Builder of Great Pyramid at Gizeh
V, VI	
VII, VIII,	
IX, X	
XI	
XII	**AMENEMHET I**
XIII **XVII**	
XVIII	**HATSHEPSUT** **TUTANKHAMEN** 12th ruler of the 18th dynasty
XIX	

Etc.: more dynasties

showed a confusing development in arts and crafts before they reached the highest point—that of the last palace.

The puzzle proved extremely hard to solve. No tablets or other clues had been found which bore names of other kings or dates. Only the name of great Minos, of the legends, was known. Perhaps Minos was a title used by all succeeding rulers, as the Egyptian rulers were called Pharaoh?

"Something strange happened at Knossos," Arthur Evans commented to a companion at the site. "It might have been a man-made disaster, yet I doubt it. I rather believe some natural catastrophe struck at Knossos."

At Knossos, there was little to prove a fate similar to that of Pompeii, yet there was evidence of sudden, overwhelming disaster. Whatever it may once have been, Knossos had ceased to live, almost overnight. Artists' tools were found beside objects they had been making when disaster struck. There were signs that people had left household tasks, meals, all sorts of things half finished. What caused them to leave their homes so hurriedly, so unprepared?

The reason for this abrupt ending to a mighty civilization was hard to find, and trying to unravel the mystery kept Arthur engrossed. At the age of fifty, he brought the accumulated knowledge and patience of a distinguished career to the most difficult task of his life.

Having decided to call the buildings The Palace of Minos, Arthur thought it logical to call the civilization Minoan, rather than the less specific Cretan. The next step, then, was to devise a system to classify and date the amazing variety of things which had already been found.

The period 3200 B.C. to about 2700 B.C., according to evidence ancient man left at the bottom of the test pits, was neolithic. How much earlier than that men had dwelt at Knossos is unknown. Arthur's estimate of ten thousand years is not unreasonable, for geologists and archaeologists are finding evidence daily of much greater age for mankind. This period, the neolithic, corresponds roughly to the Egyptian reign of Pharaoh Menes dynasty. (see table)

The second groping stage toward civilization, from 2700 B.C. to 2100 B.C., Arthur labeled Early Minoan. The strata evidence showed several periods of rise and fall in this time. It became necessary, therefore, to subdivide Early Minoan into periods I, II, and III. The cups, pottery, tools and weapons, the ornaments and figurines, varied in skills, colors used, and methods of manufacture.

The shaky ground beneath the feet of the man working back in time grew steadier. From 2100 B.C. to 1600 B.C., Arthur called Middle Minoan. A much higher stage of civilization had been reached by now. Yet, once again, there were the mysterious breaks. Arthur had to subdivide into Middle Minoan I, II, and III. He was becoming suspicious of these peculiar breaks in continuity of the lives of the ancient Minoans. And from his suspicion, the germ of an idea, a possible solution to this puzzle, began to stir his thinking.

From 1600 B.C. to 1200 B.C., was the finest and last flowering of Minoan civilization. Egyptian evidence, left by Pharaohs Amenemhet I, Sesostris I, and others, finally brought the time traveler, Arthur Evans, safely to his destination. But he found that even Late Minoan, as he called this last period, suffered from mysterious breaks in continuity. Then, suddenly, this marvelous civilization had ceased to exist. Why? And how?

The tantalizing puzzle nagged at the archaeologist detective. Then, miraculously, the answer clicked in Arthur's mind. In a flash of intuition, he believed he had solved the puzzle, learned the cause of the breaks and the reason for the devastation that plagued the Minoans.

But intuition, belief in the rightness of one's deductions, is not proof. Arthur had no concrete evidence to back his theory. Being a wise and sound scholar, a scientific researcher, Arthur kept his thoughts to himself for the time being. Perhaps, as his work progressed, he would find the evidence he sought. With his timetable forming the skeleton, at least he could begin to put flesh on the bones of his suspicions.

There was proof of constant trading between ancient Egyptians and Minoans. Some ancient Egyptian had learned to make a kind of paper from a plant that grew beside the river Nile. The method lasted until well into the fourth century A.D. Had the Minoans, too, known this secret? Why, then, had only clay tablets so far been found? Certainly, records of stores would need to be kept on a material more substantial than papyrus, but they might have used papyrus for their songs and plays, their poetry, their history. The remains of an amphitheater, better known now as the Theatral Area, could be seen at Knossos. Some scholars are now inclined to think that this Theatral Area is a monumental entranceway, the central court of the various buildings, perhaps the site of the "bull games." Might some papyrus records yet be found? Or had all papyrus been totally destroyed when Knossos met her doom? Dried beans had been found in jars, the same kind of beans still grown in Egypt. Why not papyrus?

The enigma of Minoan writing remained as inscrutable as the sphinx. Arthur worked very hard to solve the riddle when he was not digging at Knossos, but ability to read the Minoan symbols eluded his understanding. And his intuition refused to help.

On the clay tablets, Arthur found primitive outlines of characters which he identified as representing men, women, animals, and other objects easily recognized. These "stick" figures, it seemed, had evolved from earlier crude pictographs. The second stage had developed into a sophisticated form of writing.

Arthur, better to understand and study the systems of writing, separated them. First, the pictographs, the earliest.

The linear scripts, Arthur found, were two distinctly different types. These he named Linear Script A, and Linear Script B. He struggled with the mystery, but drew no further meaning from the symbols. Yet fate was kind.

He *did succeed,* wonderfully, in deciphering the symbols Minoans used for counting, and numbering.

UNITS

/ = 1   thus ///// = 5

TENS

● or ▬ or ▬▬ = 10

thus ●●●● , ▬▬▬ , ▬▬▬▬ = 50

HUNDREDS

O = 100   thus OOOOO = 500

THOUSANDS

⟡ = 1000   thus ⟡⟡⟡⟡ = 4000

EXAMPLE

⟡⟡OOOO≡≡≡///// =: 2496

Minoan system of numerals discovered
and interpreted by Sir Arthur Evans

It began to appear that the clay tablets were lists of stores. This became more clear after Arthur had found out how the Minoans counted. Some tablets bore pictures inscribed with number symbols. An arrow with numbers showed how many arrows were kept in the storage places. Some tablets bore what seemed to represent ears of grain.

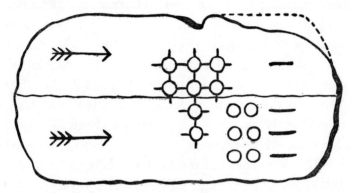

Example of clay tablets found at Knossos. This tablet of baked clay shows a storage of 8,640 arrows

Hope was high that dates and names of other kings might appear, but the Minoans remained silent.

All the evidence accumulated made it certain that the archaeologists had hardly scratched the surface of the kingdom of Minos. If the work was to proceed, and it must, funds would have to be raised. The excitement the discovery had created in England made Arthur feel it would be easy to collect money for the work, but it proved not to be so.

Military adventures in India, the Middle East, and elsewhere put a heavy drain on the pockets of Britons. The war with the Dutch Boers in South Africa was raging. A young war correspondent, Winston Churchill, monopolized headlines in newspapers. Churchill, too, had been a student at Harrow School. He, too, had not been considered a particularly successful student. He had electrified his countrymen by a daring escape from a Boer prison camp, becoming a national hero in the process. The Boers put a heavy price on his head. The very same year Arthur Evans made his discovery of the Minoans, Winston Churchill was elected to Parliament. He continued a stormy career and frequently monopolized the headlines.

With all these matters demanding attention, Britons had neither the time nor the patience to heed the wonder of Knossos. There was no radio or television to spread the word. People even forgot the sporadic fighting in the Balkans. Arthur, though still banished, kept abreast of developments. He shook his head in wonderment. The explosion he feared was not far off. Agonizingly, he wondered aloud, "How can people be so blind?" But the way of the prophet is hard, and he and Churchill both soon discovered this truth.

With the little support he did get, Arthur dipped into his own pockets more deeply. Fortunately, he received several legacies and his father, still a very wealthy man, was a staunch supporter.

As season slipped into season on Crete, a form of architecture was revealed to the world which had never been seen before. The site of the palace spread until it covered an amazing area of six acres!

Unlike the buildings of ancient Greece and Rome, the Minoan architecture developed to this high state with materials at hand. Wood played an important part in construction. Once, in the dim past, Crete *must* have been well wooded. Some of the timbers used in construction, whole tree trunks, were found to be supporting weights of five tons of masonry and more, and the whole plastered over.

There was no doubt that palaces had been built upon the foundations of earlier structures, because alterations from several periods had frequently been made. The materials and workmanship of these alterations furnished important clues to the time of the changes. For a long time, it was difficult to piece together an accurate picture of the original buildings. The floors and walls had evidence of being damaged and repaired. There were many signs of destruction by fire, but not always was fire the cause of damage. But what was the other cause? Still, Arthur kept his suspicions to himself.

As rooms were cleared, Arthur and his colleagues had to resort to the kind of propping used in deep mining, since one room often revealed another below. He ordered iron girders shipped from England, but due to poor facilities for unloading in the harbor at Candia, these girders often splashed to the harbor bottom in several fathoms of water.

As each level was cleared and floors and ceilings propped up, an astounding building of several stories, at least five, was revealed. Great light wells brought illumination to the lower levels. These light wells, being centrally placed in the building, also served to keep out the strong and bitter winds of winter. Working outward from these light wells, clearing rubbish from rooms and corridors leading

off them, an incredibly modern way of life was revealed.
Pushing on, the diggers found that the palace had a do-
mestic quarter, audience and throne rooms, storage rooms,
and places for worship and ritual ablutions.   Several altars, some still with traces of offerings and the figurines
of gods and goddesses on them, were discovered.   Royal
property seemed to be indicated by the ever-recurring
symbol of the double axe.

The palace boasted an amazingly modern drainage system, which led to the discovery of bathrooms, with elaborate hip baths of baked and glazed clay, beautifully
designed and elaborately painted.   Water was piped from
natural springs on higher ground.   The terra cotta drain
pipes were gracefully tapered and fitted together with
"sleeves" or overlapping joints that were cemented to-

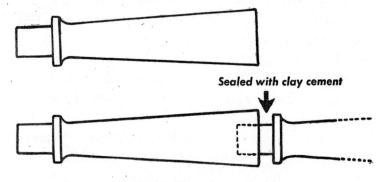

*Minoan drainage tiles from
the Palace of Minos at Knossos*

gether.   The tapering shape of the drain pipes, which can
compare favorably with any modern drain tiles, gave an

added thrust to the water passing downward and through them. Wastes from bathrooms were flushed away in a surprisingly modern manner. Again, the tapered shape of the drain pipes, working with gravity, carried off the wastes to a lower level disposal area. Probably, natural-acting bacteria finally broke up the wastes, much as it does in rural and farm areas today where septic tanks are commonly used. All this intricate system of piped water and drainage clearly indicated the Minoans had some knowledge of hydraulics and knew how to manipulate water for their purposes.

The most fantastic discovery of all was the finding of parts of the "Bull Jumping Fresco." It was restored by M. Guilleron. Here, amazingly, was shown the germ of truth behind the legend of Theseus and the Minotaur! Bulls played an important role in the lives of Minoans. But what was that role?

Arthur marveled as he feasted his eyes on the slim boy and girl acrobats painted by the ancient artists, incredibly lifelike, grappling with the fierce bulls. Their movements were simply unbelievable. Similar scenes occurred on pottery and seals and rings. Some of the scenes resembled bareback riding seen in modern circuses. Would anyone today try handling a savage bull as these boys and girls of Knossos had? A boy and girl, working in a team, ran or danced up to the bull, then seized his great horns. One vaulted lightly over his head and somersaulted over his back into the waiting arms of a partner running behind the racing animal. What did all this mean? Were these beautiful young people the youths and maidens taken in tribute from Athens? Arthur was mystified, but vastly intrigued.

Almost in compensation for the lack of written records, the discovery of more and more frescoes, brilliantly painted in a wide range of colors and finely detailed, told much of the daily life of this ancient people.

One day, Arthur was sitting quietly on a broken column. In his hands he held a newly found vase. Suddenly, the shout of a workman broke into his thoughts. Panting, the Moslem worker rushed up to Arthur.

"Effendi!" ("Sir!"), he cried. "You come! You come quick!"

Thinking something tragic had happened, Arthur hurriedly followed the man into the place where they were working. Several workmen were kneeling on the floor in a room they were clearing of debris. As he drew near, Arthur Evans gasped. Immediately he took charge, and knelt gently on the floor.

Delicately, Arthur brushed at the earth. With each stroke his eyes widened. Under his trembling hands emerged a glittering jeweled mosaic. Gold showed—crystal, silver, and ivory inlay. "Careful, careful," Arthur cautioned as the workers jostled each other for a closer look. "It's very fragile."

When all the dirt was brushed away, the beautifully jeweled mosaic, approximately three and a half feet long and two feet wide, seemed to wink and shimmer at the men who had brought it from its dark centuries of burial.

Some kind of plaster border and backing held the gold, silver, crystal and ivory pieces in the position of its design.

"I do believe," Arthur said, "it's a game board of some kind. Imagine—perhaps great Minos himself played at this board!"

"Whoever owned it was certainly a wealthy one!" grunted a workman.

Turning to a colleague, Arthur asked, "How on earth are we going to get it up from the floor?"

"Um! Yes," his colleague ruminated. "It's going to be a tricky job. We'll never get it back to its original design. Let's put our heads together and see what we can invent."

A conference was held, and a very clever answer to the problem emerged. A wooden form was built all around the edges of the beautiful game board. The gap between the form and the game board was then filled with strong plaster. Later, when this had hardened and set, slivers of wood were eased gently under the board. As it slowly raised from the ground, more plaster was pushed into the gaps underneath it. It was tedious work, and two long days elapsed before it was finished.

Triumphantly, the lovely mosaic was lifted from the floor. How many centuries had it rested there? It had been damaged when rubble had collapsed on it, but here it was again, not one bit the worse for having been rescued. It was strong enough now; later it could be cleaned properly and restored to its true splendor.

As more of the wooden structural parts of the palace of Minos were uncovered, an interesting piece of the puz-

zle of Minoan life fell into place.   Pottery, tools, and
golden ornaments showed a strong resemblance to objects
which Arthur had examined at Mycenae, on the Greek
mainland.   Had the Minoans then, known and traded
with Mycenae?   Yet the resemblance was *too* marked between goods and weapons used at Knossos and Mycenae.
There must have been close cultural connection.   Had one
city been a colony of the other?   If this were so, then Mycenae, since it was not as old as Knossos, must have been settled by Minoans.   The frescoes bore out a relationship in
their border designs.   Objects found at Mycenae, like the
strange seal rings must have come from Knossos.   The
figure eight shield motif, which had so puzzled Schliemann
when he found it on pottery and other things at Mycenae,
now appeared as floor-to-ceiling wall decorations in a great
room at the Palace of Minos!   An important link in the
chain of evidence had been forged by the recurrence of
these man-sized shields.

As they uncovered more rooms, Arthur began to worry.
"We must find something," he said, "to protect what we
are exposing to the elements.   These floors and walls and
ceilings with their soft gypsum plaster paneling will not
survive long in Cretan winters.   Hard rain and blustering
winds will pit them beyond all recognition."

From this concern for preservation, Arthur Evans
evolved a method that had never before been used in archaeology.   It has stood the test of time.   It showed too
the wisdom of having a trained architect to work with him.
A great columned room, now called the Hall of the Columns, had started the train of thought.   Several rooms,

corridors, and traces of flights of stairs led off this great hall.

If the archaeologists were to dig their way to the lower floors and down the stairs, something more than pit props was needed to hold the floors and ceilings above them. It was work that could, in fact, *must* be done simultaneously with the excavating. And if it were not done, the whole edifice so painstakingly emerging from the earth, would collapse into a senseless heap of rubble.

Arthur knew that reinforced concrete was coming into its own as a highly fluid and useful building material. After a discussion with his colleagues, it was decided to try the material at Knossos.

It proved to be an inspired choice. Floors at the top were spread with a layer of concrete. The ceilings of rooms below were thus protected and made firm. And on down the stairs they went. Columns holding the stairs were checked for exact measurements and position. Every tiny detail of workmanship was noted and sketched. When burned or rotted columns were replaced by concrete, then painted in the original colors, they looked almost exactly as they must have looked when Minos trod the stairs in the days of his glory.

The new material proved easy and efficient. Wood forms, where needed, could be knocked together at the site. The sand and cement, the steel reinforcing rods, could all be handled more easily. And, wonder of wonders, it proved cheaper than any other method they considered.

The Hall of the Columns was rebuilt, its columns and

windows replaced. Whenever possible, original materials were wedded to reconstructions. Another room, close by, was reconstructed, including in the "new" work the original parts of panels and painted plaster found lying about in the rubble.

As digging drew to a close for a time, Arthur was well content. He had at last found himself, found his life's work. His papers on the discoveries and his theories were being widely read. With great satisfaction, he learned that he had been elected a Fellow of the Royal Society. Arthur and his father, Sir John, were the first concurrent father and son members of the Society in all its long and bright history.

All was not, however, honor and glory. As time passed, some scholars criticized Arthur forcefully. They objected to his fine reconstruction work. While his critics were fair enough to admit he spent large sums of money from his own funds for the work, they accused him of gratifying his own desires. He was twitted for being a "rich man's son." Some of his critics felt it was enough to save the objects found. Some of the criticism was natural jealousy of Arthur's brilliant success, but much of it was the result of the eternal resentment against what is new. It is not difficult to see what might have happened to the many-storied palace of Minos had Arthur Evans not been bold enough to use the means of preservation he did. Today, it might well be nothing more than a heap of rubbish.

It is fortunate for us that Arthur persisted in his own manner. He did his best to ignore the complaints which he knew were unjustified. Where criticism was honest and impersonal, he tried to make good use of it. And the very great care with which the sketches, restorations, highly detailed descriptions, were recorded and published, proves his work and methods far more than the mere whim of a rich man. Inevitably there were mistakes made. These could always be corrected by honest researchers later, after Arthur's great pioneering was over.

There were still other troubles. Many of Arthur's old antagonists at Oxford were still active. They grew petty and grumbled about his long absences from the Ashmolean. Mr. Bell warned Arthur of small irritations which kept breaking out, indicating future troubles of a more serious nature. Being so passionately convinced of the value of what he was doing, and of the importance to archaeology, to all learning, of Knossos, Arthur found it difficult to be patient. He fought back when he thought he should, but with each passing day he felt more sure that he must give up his keepership of the Ashmolean and devote full time to Crete.

ELEVEN

Hectic Years

ARTHUR EVANS, a man touched by genius, was a paradox. Many qualities blended contentedly in his personality. He was an extremely practical man, yet a visionary and dreamer. He could appear to be a man with all the flair of a dashing adventurer, while basically he was exceedingly modest. Sometimes he could be a gentle human being, still he had a temper and often appeared autocratic and overbearing.

The violently changing times in which Arthur lived his life helped shape the man. The calm gentility of the last half of the nineteenth century had given way to the raucous twentieth century. Arthur was not the only man bewildered by the changing times in which he lived.

Margaret Freeman had been the love of his life. It never seemed to occur to Arthur that he might marry again, and he never did. Knossos was his love now. Children had been denied to him and Margaret, yet he loved children with a passion. Such love seeks expression, and by some magic, children were drawn to the kindly, slightly stooped figure, and Arthur always felt completely at ease with them. The unfettered imaginations of young people warmed his own heart.

Arthur's years were now filled with feverish activity. He found time to help establish a boy scout troop which took its name from his house. The Youlbury troop had free access to the woods and grounds, using them for nature studies, camping, and other activities. Arthur Evans was happy to hear his woods ringing with their shouts of pleasure and excitement. Whenever he could, he joined them, as much a boy as any.

Arthur's fame was bright and shining, but new honors did not affect him, except to add dignity to his bearing. It was with great pride that Sir John heard his son read papers to their society. Arthur's halting manner of speech and his platform presence had magnetism. This stemmed from sincerity, conviction, and sure knowledge of the subjects he studied. He made past ages live again in his word pictures, because he loved and admired the efforts of men who created civilizations at the dawn of history. His humorous mouth and twinkling eyes gave him an elfin look, and his small frame aided the illusion. Yet his temper, when he fought injustice, or battled for what he believed right, was most stinging for those upon whom it was turned.

Other archaeologists, from Italy, America, France, and

Germany, were making equally astonishing discoveries on the island of Crete. Their work proved that the whole island had once been a highly developed and traveled land. All this had to be related to Arthur's own studies, and the task was formidable. More and more of Arthur's attention was demanded at Crete, yet he could not quite relinquish his interest in the Ashmolean to which he gave so many of his years.

Arthur Evans solved the problem of his keepership very neatly. He resigned, actively, but got himself appointed Honorary Keeper. This gave him a permanent voice in the affairs of the museum, but freed him from troubling and time-consuming details. Now he was free to get on with other things.

In these hectic years, Arthur found time to stand for Parliament, to the astonishment of his many friends. He was soundly beaten in the election, but emerged from the experience none the worse. It was a good thing he was beaten, for he had neither the thick skin nor the compromising ability necessary for success in politics, and politics might have kept him from Knossos.

Arthur was made a trustee of the British Museum. And throughout his crowded weeks spent hours trying to decipher the Minoan tablets, but made little progress beyond understanding their numbers.

And the big world beyond crept closer. Older members of the Evans family were dying off. The world was changing. The Balkans were once more flaming and Arthur watched events with sad interest. Austria annexed Herzegovina to its Empire, paving the way for the explosion that was not long coming. The small Balkan countries and Greece, to the great surprise of the big powers, banded together and finally drove the Turks from their countries. Large and small powers began to maneuver to fill the vacuum left by the departed Turks.

Sir John Evans, whose health was failing, turned over his immense and valuable collection of old coins and prehistoric artifacts to Arthur. Sir John's treasures would be well cared for by his son. But his mind was still alive and active despite poor health, and he managed, occasionally, to read a paper to his societies. His life had been full indeed, and he had accomplished much. He also had the satisfaction of watching his example bear the fruit of greatness in his son. Arthur was now quite rich. Several relatives left him estates in their wills, and finally, with the childless death of old John Dickinson's last son, he inherited that estate as well.

In May, 1908, Sir John Evans died, tired, and heavy with the eighty-five years of a full life. He left his son richer than ever, but the death was a severe blow to Arthur. Had it been possible, he would gladly have exchanged his great wealth to keep his father by his side.

At times, it seemed as if all the world were going mad. The Evans clan, lovers of gracious living and learning, had now shrunk greatly. The Victorian era was gone, and even the showy Edwardian era was about finished. Arthur Evans now had a motor car, which he loved to drive

as fast as he could get it to go. Perhaps, in this way, he
worked out of his own system the fever that was attacking
his world.

The short gaiety of the Edwardian era ended, and the
sober reign of George V began. In 1911, George V of England and his great Queen Mary were crowned in West-
minster Abbey. In the honors list celebrating the coro-
nation, Arthur Evans was knighted. He became Sir
Arthur Evans, in honor of his services to his country and
science.

In 1914, the fast moving flames touched the explosives
that set the whole world alight! Archduke Francis Fer-
dinand, heir to the throne of Austria-Hungary, was as-
sassinated at Sarajevo in Serbia. Overnight, Europe was
plunged into four years of horror. The ugly conflict
spread until the United States of America was embroiled.
Nothing so terrible had been seen since the American
Civil War, the first of all "modern" wars.

On the poppy-strewn fields of France, millions of men
huddled in trenches. And millions died, British, French,
German, Belgian, American, and others, in the awful
senseless battles whose purpose it was to gain a few feet
of ground.

Sir Arthur Evans, now sixty-three years old, could not
fight. Yet he plunged into the battles in his own way. His
knowledge of Balkan affairs and people was of great value
to his government. A band of refugees from Ragusa was
being roughly treated in England. Suspicion ran high
and fears of "spy!" touched everybody. With strongly

worded petitions, Sir Arthur badgered every official he knew on behalf of these unhappy refugees. He was so adamant, and his influence so highly respected, that he won his way.

The government turned the refugees over to Sir Arthur for safekeeping. He quartered them at Youlbury, delighted to be able to return some of the hospitality he had enjoyed from them in earlier years.

Airplanes were proving a very useful military weapon. The newly-created British Air Board, predecessor of the R.A.F., was searching for a home. They spied the strong buildings of the British Museum. "Ah, yes," they said, "that's just what we want!"

They reckoned without Sir Arthur Evans. He raved and stormed at every official who came within reach of his words, making good use of the still effective "Prodger." The savagery of war must not be allowed to destroy all the fruits built up in the years of peace. "How dare they?" he demanded. "The British Museum is more precious to me than my life! Government offices indeed. Let the Air Board look elsewhere!"

Sir Arthur rushed about England to enlist the support of every scholar and wise man he could reach. "The museum," he urged, "belongs to the people. There are plenty of buildings the Air Board can take over. The British Museum houses art and history gathered from all over the world, collected to enrich our people and enlarge their cultural awareness. Housed in the museum are the treasures of the ages! Think, just for a moment, of the immense human effort this represents! *We cannot allow these new barbarians to destroy and disperse this!"*

And the Air Board did not disperse the treasures of the British Museum. Sir Arthur's beliefs prevailed. The Air Board had to look elsewhere for a home!

War weary people in all lands of Europe dragged their tired feet toward the dreary end of 1918. Sir Arthur Evans was immensely pleased when he was summoned to sit in on the conferences of peace as a Balkan expert. Out of these conferences came the modern state of Yugoslavia, and Sir Arthur was not entirely happy with this result. He believed it wrong, ethnologically, to lump so many races into one state. Events later proved how well he knew the peoples he so long championed. "Still," he said to a friend, "it is pleasant to know I can again visit Ragusa."

The war years were sad ones for Sir Arthur. When he was not battling to right some wrong, he grappled with his great store of information from Knossos. But it was hard to concentrate. Every day brought him news of fresh tragedies. Few people cared about or had time for archaeology.

Oxford itself was a strange and deserted place. Its brightest young were being slaughtered on the battlefields of Flanders. Through it all, Sir Arthur fought for intellectual freedom, struggling to preserve reason which others threw to the winds. He had known and worked with many Germans. If vengeance were allowed to dominate the peace, a tragic loss to science would follow. But the prophet of doom might as well have remained silent, for a vengeful peace was gained, which carried the seeds of its own destruction.

In the last year of the war, Sir Arthur at last found it possible to return to Crete. There was consolation for him there. At sixty-seven he could reflect, from the distance of his years, that destruction comes and goes. Men's passions must have their way; but here, with the pots and tablets, the relics of a long dead civilization, he realized anew that the best in the human spirit was too vital ever to be destroyed completely.

Love for his boy scouts, sadness at the bitter long war's toll, affected Sir Arthur deeply. He had a monument erected at Youlbury for which he composed an inscription, drawing from his own great heart. The words carved on the sundial and seat memorial read:

> In loving memory of a youthful band
> Who played as children
> Among these woods and heaths,
> And shared, at Youlbury, in joyous hours:
> In the Great War
> For their country's sake and for mankind:
> They fell before their time:
> But, wherever they now lie,
> Here, they are never very far.

By the time 1921 arrived, the world was becoming accustomed to peace, and a tremendous surge of activity took place on the island of Crete.

The first volume of Sir Arthur Evans's great work, *The Palace of Minos at Knossos,* published in 1921, aroused considerable excitement among scholars. It was fortunate for Sir Arthur that his publisher was also his good friend. George Macmillan, of the famous publishing house bearing his family name, was a dedicated follower of archaeology. The publisher's venture was extremely expensive, but George Macmillan believed firmly in the value of knowledge contained in such books. He did not expect to make money from the book. Even so, there were times he raged about Sir Arthur in his office.

"What does the man think he is up to? More notes, more changes! This must stop! We're ready for the presses!"

Sir Arthur's desire for accuracy had become almost a vice. Until the last day before printing, he bombarded Macmillan with corrections, errata, alterations, and masses of detailed work. Sir Arthur still used his old quill pen, which did not help the confusion.

Maria and Joan Evans looked on with a mixture of affectionate amusement and exasperation. Fortunately for Sir Arthur, twenty-nine year old Joan Evans was rapidly becoming a well-known scholar herself, reaffirming the Evans tradition. She was immensely valuable to her half-brother in indexing his great work and keeping check on organization of the vast store of material. Sir Arthur loved her for it, and as time passed leaned heavily upon her assistance.

Maria worried about him. "His house is almost like a museum itself," she said to Joan. "How the man ever gets anything done is quite beyond me. I'm sure that half the time he forgets to eat properly or regularly, though he says he does."

Wisely, except for an occasional word of caution to look after himself more carefully, Maria did not interfere.

The growing piles of notes grew bigger. Room, more room was the constant demand at Youlbury. Sir Arthur made additions to his house. When a new category for his material seemed necessary, he simply set up another table. He sorted his material into piles on the tables, then hopped around them for whatever he wanted to find at that moment. It was not the most efficient system, but it suited Sir Arthur. He was supremely happy wandering among this huge jumble. To him, it all made good sense.

In Crete, the Turkish house Sir Arthur had bought in 1900 to use as headquarters proved crowded and unhealthy in the fever-ridden valley. Sir Arthur, therefore, had a new headquarters built closer to the palace, and a watch tower to overlook the site. Once installed in the new house, which he called Villa Ariadne, he felt more secure, closer to the past he was still bringing back to life. The house is still used by the British School and many famous archaeologists live there while they work at Crete.

Sir Arthur Evans had thought the excavations were close to being exhausted in the early twenties. But he was wrong. The years rolled along, and up came more of the astonishing city of Knossos. It was seen, as the archaeologists carefully followed the walls, that an immense city lay waiting beyond the palace buildings. The city and its cemeteries were gradually outlined and cleared of rubble. Roads of a highly scientific design were found, showing that the cities of the island had been well connected. But not one scrap of literature appeared. All that was known of the clothes, toiletries, customs, and the rituals of Minoans was what could be seen in their glorious frescoes.

Patiently, Sir Arthur worked on his theories and interpretations of the thousands of utensils, objects of art, and the other massive evidence he collected. Slowly, like a giant jigsaw puzzle, he pieced together the outline, filled in the fine detail of Minoan life. Everything concerning them, from cradle to grave, their religious beliefs, came under his scrutiny.

For those who do not have the "inner eye" to see how things once were, it is indeed fortunate that Sir Arthur insisted on reconstruction at the Palace of Minos. Through his team of archeologists, architects, artists, and workmen, great portions of the palace were returned to their original glory. So brilliantly colorful, so full of life and movement, and so awe inspiring were these reconstructions that visitors gazed in astonishment at the civilization nobody had believed really existed.

Then, suddenly, something happened that made Sir Arthur Evans's blood run cold!

TWELVE

The Roaring Minotaur Returns

IN JULY, 1926, Sir Arthur was reading in his bed at Knossos. It had been a pleasant day, and warm. He was happy. Work progressed well, and several pleasant additions to the pottery collection had been uncovered. But he was growing sleepy.

Then, about nine-thirty, the ground began to sway, gently. Small articles and books fell from shelves and tumbled about the floor.

Suddenly, the swaying of the earth grew more fearsome, and Sir Arthur jumped from his bed. Like an insistent, red flashing light, the word, "Earthquake!" lit his mind.

A quiver of mixed elation and fear swept through Sir Arthur's taut body: had he been right? Was this the proof, the evidence he had needed so long to give weight to the intuition he'd experienced so many years before—*the reason for the puzzling breaks in the lives of the Minoans?*

Though he had said very little about his notions, Sir Arthur had unconsciously been expecting something like this for years.

The shocks grew steadily more severe. The earth began to sway, making dreadful sounds like *the angry roaring of a bull!* Sir Arthur, believing his new house would hold together, stayed where he was. He looked out toward the Palace of Minos and the resurrected city of Knossos. He trembled, fearful for the enormous effort and expenditures that had gone into the excavations and restorations. He prayed for the safety of his life's work.

A huge column of dust rose into the dark velvet sky, completely blocking out the moon. The eerie light was awesome to behold. Sir Arthur observed closely from his window, acutely aware of the significance of what was happening. Did he imagine it, or was the palace swaying? He could not see too well.

Screams filled the darkness from a distance, sounding like the despair of lost souls. A few houses collapsed, adding the cracking, tearing noise to the weird sounds of the dark night. Churches in nearby Candia cracked, and badly damaged steeples toppled to the ground, adding more dust to the air. People rushed wildly into the open spaces, frightened for their lives. Transfixed, shocked, they huddled in groups to watch the fantastic movements of trees on the heaving bosom of the earth.

Then, again and again, with his own ears, Sir Arthur Evans heard the *"bellowing of the bull, deep in the labyrinth."*

A sluggish dawn, breaking into the dust-laden, heavy, dark sky, gradually illuminated the Palace of Minos and the city of Knossos. A sigh of relief escaped Sir Arthur's lips. His beloved city and palace had not returned to the rubble from which he had rescued them. He gave thanks to God. The reconstruction work, the stout reinforced concrete, had withstood the angry earth's onslaught. All was well at Knossos. Not so at the museum in Candia where many treasures of Minos rested. Some of the frescoes and other antiquities kept there had been fractured and badly damaged.

His head buzzing with thoughts that would not come clear, Sir Arthur wandered through the palace. He could almost feel the hot breath of the Minotaur. As his thoughts cleared, wonderment at the confirmation of his theory invaded his mind.

Under the inevitable impetus of war, science made great forward strides. A large store of new knowledge was given to the world, but much which we take for granted today was still unknown in the twenties and thirties of our century.

Sir Arthur was sure that the palace had more than once been burned and wrecked before it finally vanished. He had put little store in the theory that Theseus, instead of being alone as the legend said, had sacked Knossos at the head of a large army from the Greek mainland. Traces of repair work from different periods in the long existence of the palace, centuries old, bore mute testimony to his own notions. Burned beams and pillars and calcified remains indicated severely destructive fires. Perhaps, after the last destruction of 1400 B.C., a few survivors had lived on in the ruins, slowly degenerating or dispersing during the centuries before the rise of Greece. In the absence of modern rescue and sustenance methods, who would there be to care for survivors of a tremendous catastrophe as this must have been. Who could protect them from the pestilence sure to follow? It was a sound theory. Earthquakes were the chief cause of the breaks in Minoan continuity, and fire often accompanied earthquakes in their dreaded mission of destruction.

Now Sir Arthur *knew* that at least seven great earthquakes had battered Knossos, and that they could be approximately dated. Four of them, he felt sure, were extremely severe, and had occurred between the last century of the third millenium and the fourteenth century B.C. The others, since it had been possible to repair the damage, could not have been so severe. Now his division of Minoan life into periods rested upon a firmer basis than ever.

Modern oceanographers, geologists, seismologists have taught us truths about our earth that were not known to men like Sir Arthur a few decades ago. They have also helped establish the probable truth of his theories. We now know that the island of Crete lies athwart a weakness in the earth's crust. Under tremendous pressures, mountains rose and continents sank below the waters. Ocean beds became plains and mountains, dry continents were

overwhelmed by oceans. Glaciers have advanced and retreated, weakening and gouging the earth and rock strata.
From all this cataclysmic movement, the fantastic pressures involved, a weakness was left in the earth. It passes
overland and under oceans.

Starting at Japan, this great earth fault can be traced
in a wide belt around the earth. It crosses the Pacific,
parts of North and South America, Mexico, across the
Atlantic to Portugal, Italy, *Crete*, Turkey, and India.
Most of these countries, and others adjoining them, have
suffered earthquakes. The island of Crete lies well
within the bounds of this fault in the earth's crust.

The great earthquake at Crete, in 1926, proved to be
of inestimable value to Sir Arthur Evans in deciphering
the riddle of Minoan beliefs. Still, it was one thing to
know this within himself, and another to put his ideas
on paper when he had thought them through, and subject his theory to the scrutiny and testing of fellow
scientists and archaeologists. Ten more years passed before he completed his great work.

During Sir Arthur's years at Knossos, another idea
gave him trouble. Some governments had grown cau-
tious about the treasures of the past hidden in their soil.
Because of this, most of the belongings of the Minoans,
which Sir Arthur and others found, remained in Crete
or Athens. Sir Arthur thought this only as it should be,
glad that governments were taking such an interest. He
was quite content to be allowed to take home duplicates,
or items the Greeks did not want to keep. He worked

intimately with the British School in Athens, and the government gave him the best of cooperation. He *did* own the site, the land itself, to do with as he pleased. And his great work of reconstruction could never be moved from the site. He could sell his land, or endow it. He was a rich man with a wide choice.

Unfortunately, there was no son to whom he could entrust his life's work, and Sir Arthur felt a great obligation to protect and preserve Knossos for future generations. How best to accomplish this? To whom, he wondered, could he pass on care of the remains of this once great people? This fountainhead of Western civilization, older by far than Greece, had immense value to scholars and students: it must be wisely protected for their sakes. He needed something more stable than a government promise, for governments come and go.

Sir Arthur's seventy-seven years hung lightly upon his shoulders. He had been too busy to notice their passing. The solution he found for his worry lay almost under his nose. The British School in Athens had integrity and an enjoyable reputation. It worked closely with Greek authorities and held their confidence. Certainly, he thought, this institution was the logical beneficiary of the property. Sir Arthur, his decision made, promptly deeded his lands to the British School at Athens.

In 1928, the second part of Sir Arthur's work, *The Palace of Minos*, was published. There was so much material in it that it had to be issued in two volumes.

Expense was so high that only a limited number of these precious books could be printed. The work was as complete as Sir Arthur could make it up to that time. It contained many corrections and revisions from the first volume. Not a scrap of pottery had been overlooked by Sir Arthur in presenting his work to the world of scholars. Such detail, such care is a monument to his devotion to his work. And still, the excavations at Knossos were incomplete. New discoveries were made each succeeding season.

Summers usually found Sir Arthur, with "Prodger," poking and swinging about Knossos. Winters, when he was not lecturing or giving a paper, he isolated himself in his house, Youlbury, working on the Minoan scripts, writing further explanations of the discoveries being made. In 1930, another earthquake, not so severe as that of 1926, rocked Knossos. The reconstruction again withstood the shocks untroubled. The incident added more evidence to Sir Arthur's confidence in his deductions.

During 1935 and 1936, Sir Arthur finally completed and published the remainder of his great study of Minoan civilization. He was eighty-five years old! These beautiful books, rich in careful detail, are today so precious that many libraries, lucky enough to possess them, keep them under lock and key! The student wishing to study them, must do so at the library. He cannot take them home. The beautiful color plates, the astonishingly faithful sketches and diagrams, maps and tables of Mr. Fyfe, Piet de Jong and others represent thirty-five years of loving and dedicated work by Sir Arthur's team.

In 1935, the British School in Athens celebrated its fiftieth anniversary. At Burlington House, in London, they held an exhibition, and looming large over a great array of speakers was Sir Arthur Evans. In his audience, unnoticed, unobtrusive, enthralled by what he heard, sat a young English schoolboy. Michael Ventris, thirteen years old, was caught! His imagination grasped the fact, and could not loose it, that after all the years of struggle, Minoan writing had still not been deciphered! The impact of this, his astonishment, was to remain with him for the rest of his life. It would have gladdened the heart of Sir Arthur had he but known that this young schoolboy was later to round out his own great work.

THIRTEEN

Bulls, Snakes and Goddesses

IT WILL BE many years before Minoan civilization is fully understood, and placed in true historical and anthropological context within the story of man. One of the most fascinating of all things concerning this people is their religious beliefs. In some areas, there is agreement upon interpretation; in other areas, there is wide disagreement.

That bulls played an important part in religious ceremony was almost immediately noted. It is possible that during the years of darkness following the destruction of Knossos, primitive Greeks hopelessly garbled basically true tales, turning them into fantastic myths and legends. A good archaeologist should always try to remember that certain human truths remain from age to age. Ideas can be manipulated, truth can be perverted, but the basic truth remains constant, and ideas cannot be killed. The Minoans, as all human beings, had their loves and hates.

They feared and dreaded, knew joy and happiness, and there was much on the earth and in the heaven above that was dark and mysterious, and to be feared. They were not *mythical*. The Minoans were an intensely alive people, glorying in their wealth and power, stabilizing their land, cultivating beauty and comfort in their daily lives. They lifted their civilization to a height in many ways unequalled by any other civilization.

Many small sanctuaries were found in the palace and elsewhere. On the altars of these places of worship, the horns of a bull were usually prominent, indicating that they were part of the rituals held at the altar. The significant horns of bulls appear to have had some special meaning for Minoans. They even form the ornament of the great staircase of the Palace of Minos, looming as a large section of the over-all design.

In the beginning, paleolithic and neolithic Cretans probably suffered often from earthquakes. No doubt, too, there were many wild or even domesticated bulls and the noises issuing from the earth during an upheaval may have terrified these primitive humans. It would be easy to imagine that a great bull lived deep in the earth. When he grew angry, he heaved his great shoulders to rip the earth and terrorize all life on the surface. Primitive sacrifice may have been made to placate him. Many religious beliefs have developed from an originally simple natural phenomenon, and somewhere in these dark mists lies the birth of the legend of Theseus and the Minotaur.

The double-headed ax, which occurs so often as a symbol of importance at the Palace of Minos, may have an equally simple origin. Ancient Cretans may have discovered that such a weapon gave them a mastery over fierce bulls. With untutored logic, they may have revered such "magic" power, placing their reverence upon the weapon itself, rather than their own cleverness in discovering its value. In time, as their civilization matured, this symbol of power and authority may have come to mean no more than royal authority—a mark to be used on things belonging or closely related to the ruler. (In our own times, we know how a crown is the symbol of royalty, used to mark royal property.)

There may well be some truth in the legend of the seven youths and maidens taken as tribute from Athens. The bull leaping frescoes, however, do not indicate that they were sacrificed. Perhaps, as bull worship evolved, it became a sports ritual with religious overtones. These youths and maidens may have been brought to Knossos and trained in the fabulously intricate sport of bull leaping. Possibly, too, as civilization developed, the bulls themselves may have been trained animals.

There is little doubt that Knossos was ruled by law and order. People, during the city's existence, had security and substance. It might be that when these youths and maidens were no longer agile enough to perform the exhausting dances and acrobatics with the bulls, they were freed. Perhaps they married Minoans and settled down to be lost within the vast mixed population described by Homer.

As we, even in our own days, have different religions

in the world, even within countries, so with Minoans there seems to have been more than one faith. A long period without earthquakes could understandably have reduced bull worship, or minimized its importance. But man must have a faith to live by. And so, in addition to bulls, Minoans developed a religion based on snake worship.

Clay tubes seem to have been made with the idea of furnishing the reptiles places in which to crawl when they had eaten. Special dishes for food designed to suit the snakes, usually appeared in special places of snake worship in Minoan households. To this very day, in re-mote parts of Greece, snakes hold a special place in the minds of rural folk, and children are severely scolded if they harm a snake. This primitive belief, too, may have a logical basis. The flowers and grasses, birds, fish, and butterflies beloved by Minoans in the wall paintings, oc-cur frequently on household utensils and decorative motifs. They worshipped and loved nature. A snake keeps close to the bosom of mother earth. It seems sim-ple enough, therefore, to deduce that closeness with the earth led Minoans to believe snakes privileged creatures with mother earth. Life itself depended upon the fruit-fulness of the earth.

Snakes have always awed and fascinated mankind. From the serpent in the Garden of Eden until today, some form of snake worship has existed. At Knossos and other places in Crete, many ancient figurines depict goddesses with snakes entwined about their bodies. One of these, a fine example, is widely known as the "Boston Goddess." She is an exquisitely lovely figure, and her antecedents are shrouded in mystery.

The "Boston Goddess" is an ivory figure about six and a half inches tall. She wears a tiara. Holes around the head indicate that at one time she wore either natural hair or gold threads simulating hair. She is robed in a tiered, flounced skirt held at the slim waist by a girdle of gold. She wears a tight-fitting jacket which completely exposes the breasts, as was Minoan custom. Her two arms, outstretched, have snakes coiled about the wrists and forearms. The heads of the snakes look up to the face of the goddess. The snakes, of gold with tongues protruding, are superb examples of the marvelous skill of Minoan goldsmiths. They are so real, the snakes seem almost to hiss!

How the goddess came to be in Boston is a mystery. This has led some people to think she may be a clever imitation. In 1914, under the sensitive hands of Mr. L.D. Caskey, the goddess was cleaned and restored to much of her original beauty. According to Mr. Caskey, the figure had come from Crete to Boston, but he claimed no knowledge of how or where she had been found. Later, Sir Arthur Evans gave an added detail or two. He stated that his friend, Mr. Richard Seagar, found the goddess in private hands in Crete, along with other objects too decayed for restoration. The inference seems to be that she was found or pilfered from Knossos or some other site and sold for private gain.

Archaeologists must be on constant guard against such pilfering. Workmen quickly get to know the value of the objects the earth gives up to their spades and picks.

But to Sir Arthur, what did it really matter how she came back to the light of day, so long as she was safe? In his own words:

None need regret that the Knossian goddess—so admirably reconstituted—should have found such a worthy resting place and that she stands today as a Minoan "Ambassadress" to the New World!

Many such figurines were found, though not all as fine as the "Boston Goddess." Some were made crudely of clay, others of precious metals and ivory. Through these figurines and other ornaments, the archaeologists learn much about the people they are studying. The occurrence of gold and ivory, silver and other precious materials not native to Crete, shows that they were a trading people. They spread throughout the Mediterranean world, trading wherever they went. There is proof that they established colonies in Sicily and Mycenae and on other parts of the Greek mainland.

Many valuable clues fell into the hands of the archaeologists. Examination of the tombs in the cemetery at Knossos revealed bodies buried with thin gold eye bandages. Were these, then, the forerunners of the elaborate gold death masks Schliemann found in the graves at Mycenae? It seems most likely.

A possible ancestry for the Minoans in Lybia, North Africa, was discovered. Some information regarding a prehistoric tribe, known as Nasamones, has come down to us from Herodotus. This ancient tribe had unusual burial customs. A dead person, probably before *rigor mortis* set in, was tightly trussed with the knees raised close under the chin. The body, thus taking up less space, was placed in a large container which was sealed before burial. There is a fine example of this kind of burial custom at the British Museum in London. The awkwardly bent mummified body is marvelously preserved. A similar custom was observed in the very early tombs at Knossos.

Another interpretation of this coincidence is that in very early times, before the sea claimed it, primitive tribes may have roamed across what might have been a "Mediterranean Plain." When waters cut off primitive tribes, they would, naturally, for a time, keep the customs they had known before.

A most valuable and important find was made at Knossos which provided wonderful clues to the life of these mysterious Minoan people. It is known as "The Town Mosaic," a picture of a Minoan town set close to the sea. Quite possibly it is a view of Knossos itself. The find was made beneath a clay and plaster pavement, upon which were found tripod pots of the Middle Minoan III period. Under this pavement, in a space between a basement room and the substructure of a portico, was a thick layer of fill dirt, in places more than seven feet thick. The mosaic, broken in pieces, was

found under this fill. Beside it, four ivory "draughtsmen" (checkers counters) were found, and the mosaic
seems to have been part of the inlay of a chest. The
"draughtsmen" might also mean that some kind of a
game like checkers was played on the mosaic—ancient
monopoly, perhaps! The chest had probably rotted
away. When the pieces of mosaic were put back together, a finely detailed view of a town was seen. The
houses were two and three stories high. They had windows of four and six panes each. In an odd way, they
resemble the black and white, wood and plaster dwellings of Tudor English houses.

When Sir Arthur contemplated his extensive work at
Crete, he drew some vital conclusions. Knossos had been
a vast city indeed. Beyond the six and a half acres of
palace buildings, the city stretched almost one mile wide,
north and south, and about the same distance east and
west. Shipping docks lay on the nearby coast area. Sir
Arthur estimated an area of more than 278 acres for the
city.

Southwest of the palace, within a radius of about 437
yards, excavation and test pits revealed well-built de-
tached housing—built as close to each other as in modern suburbs. These houses appeared to be those of upper
classes or wealthier citizens of Knossos. A similar group-
ing was discovered on the north side of the palace. It
was more difficult to reason what these buildings might
have been. At one time a Greco-Roman town had been

built in the same place, and the ruins were badly jumbled. Sir Arthur could not allow the Greco-Roman town destroyed, thus making it difficult to probe deeper into that specific area.

Knossos was built in three circles. The palace group itself; ringed around the palace were the dwellings of rich people; beyond these another ring with poorer class houses. The regular size of the houses in general, led Sir Arthur to think that perhaps legislation enforced building restrictions on the people. It is possible that fear of earthquakes lay behind the limitation of size in construction.

In some parts of Crete, Minoan dwellings were built in blocks, somewhat like city tenements. At Knossos, however, most dwelling were separated by small spaces. Again, earthquakes may have been the reason. Each of the more elaborate houses had a total area of about 263 square yards. The poorer class houses seem to have been limited to an area of about 155 square yards.

Pondering these facts, Sir Arthur tried to estimate how large a population Knossos may have had. From the size of the houses and the fact that they were usually two or more stories high, he thought it reasonable to consider eight persons to a house. He cut this figure to allow for the palace itself and believed that sixteenth century B.C. Knossos must have held a *wealthy* population of about 12,000 people! This figure is based on the number of better-class dwellings and an estimated number of people living in them.

The parts of Knossos occupied by the homes of poorer Minoans was divided by lanes and alleys. Some block construction was noted here. The area of this class of dwelling was three times the size of that occupied by rich homes. Knowing that poorer people usually have to live in crowded conditions, Sir Arthur estimated that Knossos must have had *a total population of close to 100,000 souls!* He took the busy docksides area into consideration in these estimates. He also noted that, in the cemeteries, for every hundred poor graves, there were only five that obviously had held richer persons.

These deductions are not accepted by all scholars. While most agree with their reasonableness, scholars seek further evidence and hope for greater accuracy.

A fine system of roads connected the important towns of Minoan Crete. Sedan chairs seem to have been the chief mode of transport for a long time. Later, chariots and horses appeared. Miniature, or toy clay carts, some four wheeled, some two wheeled, chariots and sedan chairs, were found in the ruins.

Minoan roads are the first example we have of well-engineered carriageways. One fine example that was excavated proved to be approximately five feet wide, with a cement coated "sidewalk," nearly three feet wide on each side of the center strip. The center strip of the road, which no doubt bore the heaviest traffic, was well designed. The under layer was built of rough stone blocks cemented together with clay cement. On top of this roadbed large stone slabs were laid. The side pavements were made with an under layer of rock slabs of irregular size, while a coating of crushed pottery and clay cement dressed the surface. Probably only foot traffic used the sidewalks.

This Minoan road was discovered at a depth of about ten feet below the present surface of the ground. And a most unexpected discovery was made here. As the archaeologists were excavating this Minoan road, they found another. At a depth of about six feet, a fine Roman road, following the same direction as the Minoan road beneath it, came to light. The Romans probably had no knowledge of the Minoan road when they built their own, for a layer of soil and rubble about four feet thick had settled atop the Minoan road.

Silent testimony to Minoan cleanliness was found in huge stone-lined pits near the palace. These pits seem to have held disposed garbage. Perhaps they worked on the same principle as the modern septic tank used in rural areas. Doubtless, from time to time, after the bacteria had reduced the bulk of the wastes, the pits were cleaned. Minoan wells, too, give proof of the engineering skill of this ancient people. Their wells were found to be lined with huge clay sections. This kept the water clean and free from rodents, and the water stayed clear and cool.

During the almost forty years of his work at Knossos, Sir Arthur developed a great respect and admiration and love for the ancient Minoan people and their incredible

achievements. His own words pay eloquent tribute to
them. In speaking of the reconstructed grand staircase
of the palace, he said:

It was my own lot to experience its strange power of imaginative suggestion, even at a time when the work of reconstitution
had not attained its present completeness. During an attack of
fever, having found for the sake of better air a temporary lodging
in the room below the inspection tower that has been erected on
the neighboring edge of the Central Court, and tempted in the
warm moonlight to look down the staircase well, the whole place
seemed to awake awhile to life and movement. Such was the force
of the illusion that the priest-king with his plumed crown, great
ladies, tightly girdled, flounced and corseted, long-stoled priests,
and, after them, a retinue of elegant but sinewy youths—as if the
Cupbearer and his fellows had stepped down from the walls—
passed and repassed on the flights of stairs below.

FOURTEEN

The Picture Clears

WHEN SIR ARTHUR EVANS published the final volume of his work at Knossos, the mass of detail took form. The quantities of pottery, figurines, clay tablets, and bronze, silver, and gold objects presented a remarkably clear picture of daily life in Knossos.

Sir Arthur had gone to Crete in 1900. By 1939, the broad clear outline of a previously unknown civilization was exposed to the eyes of an astonished world.

Puzzle after puzzle had been solved. It had perplexed the archaeologists when walls were first found—walls not far beneath the surface of the ground. But they were the walls of buildings. Nowhere were any great defensive walls seen. From earliest times, even at Troy, walled strongholds were a basic principle of safety and defence. This notion lasted until well into the middle ages, when gunpowder made strong walls obsolete. But at Knossos they had no defensive walls. Why?

The answer was found in several ways. Most importantly, perhaps, traces of the remains of Minoan ships were found. Seals and carved stones frequently bore pictures of fish-tailed ships. With gold and ivory from Africa and quaint antiquities from other parts of the Mediterranean area, it was obvious that the Minoans had been a great trading people. Apparently they commanded the Mediterranean and sailed over it as they wished. Their fleet must have been so powerful and so feared that defensive walls were not needed to protect Knossos. And there was Talos, the enormous robot!

No proof has been found of any name of a ruler other than Minos. Minos is an old name, and the ancient Greeks were awed by tales of him. Whether this was a title for the ruler, as with Pharaoh, remains a matter for conjecture unless other evidence is found, and since work still goes on in Crete, that is quite possible.

Zeus is supposed to have been born in a cave on Mount Ida. The legend held that bees had fed him honey. A goat, Amalthea, suckled Zeus with her milk. Great Minos was said to be the son of Zeus. Near the site of Knossos, in the Idean mountains, caves were found containing traces of things that may once have been offerings to gods supposedly dwelling in the caves. These legends lived on, after Knossos vanished, with the remnants of their culture. This culture, in turn, gave birth to Greek culture centuries later, which grew from colonies planted by Minoan seamen and traders.

The world owes a great debt to Sir Arthur Evans and his colleagues. His foresight in having so many experts to help in his work produced the wonderful sight that meets the eyes of modern man beholding this most ancient of civilizations. Around a huge rectangular courtyard rises the many-storied Palace of Minos. At the time of its greatest glory, all power was concentrated at this great center. The palace itself might have been the labyrinth of Daedalus. Great corridors and rooms and halls ramble in a bewildering maze.

In many rooms and halls, the fabulous frescoes have been restored, very close to their original glory. Another link to ancient Egypt is found in a fresco called, "The Captain of the Blacks." This fresco shows a light skinned Minoan leading a troop of black skinned Africans. Minos, perhaps, copying the pharaohs, liked to have a troop of exotic African soldiers to lend color to his bodyguard. The Minoans had a wide range of colors at their disposal and they used them lavishly. These frescoes tell a good deal about daily life and the routine of the court.

By their presence at boxing and wrestling matches, and other festive occasions, pictured in many frescoes, Minoan women are thought to have enjoyed great freedom. A most remarkable detail is the style of dress they wore. As painted in several frescoes, these women would have been at home in nineteenth century Paris. One of the best paintings with women pictured, a court lady with her companions, is even known as "La Parisienne."

Minoan women were dainty creatures. They had dark liquid eyes. Thick hair, curled elaborately, crowned their heads. Their fashion in dress shows they had grown wealthy, and perhaps lazy in the comfort of their days. The bodices are cut, and worn with the breasts completely exposed. Yet the style is not too different from the low-cut necklines popular in the France of the Napoleons and slightly later periods.

Minoan men, too, were astonishing creatures. Slender waists seem to have been a matter of great concern and desire. Male costume, except for ceremonial occasions, is very attractive and scanty. Some kind of waist band, perhaps of rolled leather or metal, held the brief clothing. A bikinilike garment was basic. This strap appears to have had protective padding in front. At the back, a small rounded piece of cloth, like an apron reversed in position, moved gracefully with the figure of the man wearing it. Necklaces were popular for men. Sometimes, as is seen in the fresco called "The Priest-King," one thigh is covered by a piece of flounced material, like a single, short trouser leg. The strong shoulders, bronzed arms, sturdy legs and torso were bare. The same fresco tells us that it was a fashion for the men to wear their hair long, with a kind of curled pigtail dangling over the front of one ear—a style also used to mark the sons of the pharaohs. This fresco of the "Priest-King" shows him wearing an elaborate headdress, perhaps his crown, topped with feather plumes. He is a figure of pride and majesty, striding against his background of flowers and grasses.

When the throne room was being excavated, traces of the outline of a wooden throne were found in what must have been its original position. A copy was made. The throne room, in its restored magnificence, is breathtaking. A lively frieze edges around the ceiling. A short, crooked corridor leading off this room is known as the dog's-leg corridor. It is believed to have led, privately, to the Queen's apartments. The elaborately painted and decorated bathtub and other objects of feminine use found in this portion of the palace shows us that the Queen lived in high style and greater cleanliness and luxury than that known to the great ladies of sixteenth and seventeenth century France.

Minoan gold and silversmiths were as good as any the world has known. Fine gold chains, of amazing delicacy, prove this fact. Beautiful silver daggers, too, came to light. The immense storage rooms testify to the wealth and commerce carried on by Minoans. Wine and oil jars still in their original places, were huge containers. Sir Arthur estimated the oil storage capacity of the palace alone at almost 80,000 gallons!

All these frescoes, painted with such expressive life and movement, show the Minoans lived a life of ease and plenty before they vanished. Youth and beauty were highly prized, and no doubt the desire of all Minoans was to stay young and lovely.

Who were these mysterious island people? Where did they come from? Did they, as some think, originate in North Africa? Or did they originate in Asia Minor as others believed? And was earthquake really the cause of their tragic fate, wiping them out overnight?

There are those men, with a mystical turn of mind, who wonder if these islanders are not the remnant of the legendary lost Atlantis, a story that will not die. Others have even speculated that survivors of the disaster may have crossed the Atlantic in their fish-tailed ships and built up the civilizations now being explored in the jungles of South America. But all this is no more than speculation.

Some men think a great battle destroyed the Palace of Minos and dispersed the people who survived. But would such a battle have had so dramatic an effect as to wipe out so many people so suddenly? Men who think some human event destroyed Knossos, search ancient records and legends seeking clues to support this view. But traces of fire in the destruction could more easily have been the result of sudden earthquakes, than battles. How else can the breaks in continuity, occurring at intervals over hundreds and hundreds of years, be so readily accounted for, except by earthquakes that are known to rock the island?

Perhaps we shall never be sure of the answer to these riddles. We may never know where the Minoans came from, nor the true cause of their destruction. Yet men continue to explore, to question, and work to find the truth.

For these scholars, and students, and for the awed bystander, Sir Arthur Evans returned to mankind, in his restorations, some of the glorious art and beauty of this vanished people. Some of the vital spirit that animated the Minoans has been finally given back to us. The Palace of Minos stands stark today, once more looking over the vast number of houses that were once the homes of its people. The immense flight of stairs, decorated with huge bulls' horns, once more sweeps up toward the heavens.

Perhaps on moonlit nights, when the air is warm and untroubled, the spirit of this great and proud people again echoes through the rooms and halls of the great palace that once knew so much glory and triumphant achievement.

The years began to bear down on Sir Arthur Evans. Most of his old friends, fellow workers, and family had gone. He was lonely. He remained active, giving papers and lectures, and watching over his scholarly interests. Then, as 1939 unfolded, his heart almost broke. The thing he had dreaded so long happened!

Fear stalked across Europe. Radio waves blared daily threats and counterthreats. The madness of totalitarianism burst upon a horrified world, and the most dreadful war mankind had yet witnessed swamped the helpless masses. The totalitarian dictator-clowns removed their masks, and the horror behind the masks haunts us still.

Eighty-eight years old, Sir Arthur was sick at heart for the young manhood that must again be sacrificed before its time. He began to give way to his infirmities. He cheerfully tolerated the treatment his doctor recommended, but in his heart he knew the end must soon come. He could look back on a lifetime of steady growth and achievement, of useful living such as few men had enjoyed. It had been a good life. And even though most of his old friends had gone before, he was still surrounded by large numbers of new friends who loved and respected him.

Winston Churchill, now Prime Minister, again monopolized the headlines. This time it was cause for gratitude to his fellow Harrovian, Sir Arthur. The somber tones of Big Ben boomed over the blacked-out streets of London. The gravelly voice of Winston Churchill took to the air waves: "I . . . have never promised . . . anything but blood, tears, toil, and sweat. . . ."

To his cousins across the Atlantic, Churchill's call was equally clear: ". . . give us the tools . . . and we will finish the job. . . ." Churchill understood, perhaps more clearly than anyone else, the guardianship of freedom had crossed the ocean to rest in the unwilling hands of America. They were the inheritors of Western civilization that had grown from Cretan roots. Great America was scarcely aware of her own giant strength and greatness. But she was not deaf—Churchill got tools and support beyond his most daring hopes.

The way ahead was hard and long and no man could foresee the end. But Sir Arthur and his countrymen, listening to the grave words of their leader, knew that he spoke for them all. They breathed a little more easily during the awful air raids. The faith in the chief, combined with confidence in America, somehow made Sir Arthur feel that no matter how long and hard the road, salvation lay at its end.

Before the end came, Sir Arthur visited his half sister, Joan. Standing together, they gazed at the misty blue hills and valleys of Wales, from which their ancestors came. "Here," Sir Arthur said, "I think I could live happily."

Sir Arthur Evans, nearly ninety, still had the inner strength to face despair and overcome bitterness toward those weaknesses in men which drive them to destroy. He worried as he gazed upon parts of the British Museum. It had sustained heavy bomb damage, and one particular part containing numismatic collections over which he had poured for many engrossing hours, had been completely destroyed.

Tales of destruction reached Sir Arthur from Crete. In mid-May, 1941, the Germans dropped masses of parachutists upon the strategic island of Crete. By the first of June, they were in control of the island. Fortunately, these tales of destruction were only rumors so far as Knossos was concerned. The suffered damage was little more than neglect due to the inability to maintain proper care and maintenance of the site. And this was a matter soon righted with the coming of peace.

Sir Arthur wondered what would become of his hundreds of friends and colleagues under the occupation of the enemy. Terrible stories of genocide (race annhilation) were coming out of Nazi Germany. In May, 1941, with heavy heart, he learned that John Pendlebury was dead, brutally shot by the Germans. He died in the vicinity of the palace while helping defend the Cretans whom he loved and admired as inheritors of a great tradition.

Sir Arthur visited London in a vain effort to discover what might be happening in Crete. All kinds of rumors reached him, and none of them helped his failing health. This time, Oxford rumbled and roared with the movement of tanks and big guns, far from the quiet of the previous war. Aircraft roared through the skies day and night.

Sir Arthur was almost in his ninetieth year, yet he mustered sufficient strength to receive a deputation of his colleagues who presented him with a fine scroll honoring his years and his accomplishments. It was a fitting tribute, telling him, among other things of their ". . . delight in commemorating his never-failing inspiration and encouragement to all workers in wide fields and wise counsel in the advancement of learning, and his devotion to the cause of freedom in thought and action. . . ."

There could be no finer or more true epitaph.

Three days after his ninetieth birthday, July 11, 1941, the great heart of Sir Arthur Evans failed.

He rests now, at Abbott's Langley Church in England, beside his beloved mother and father.

FIFTEEN

Bright Burns the Torch

STRANGELY, perhaps, young Michael Ventris did not take the science of philology for his career. He became an architect. Yet the study of languages remained a passion all his days. For years, in every spare moment, he studied the problem of deciphering Minoan writing.

Michael Ventris was not the only scholar searching for meaning in the clay tablets. Happily for him, and for us, these researchers exchanged their theories and findings freely.

Ventris was severely handicapped for a time. He had access to only a few of the clay tablets. There were not enough to give him a wide basis for comparison of symbols.

The famous Rosetta Stone, found in Egypt, bears a message carved in the ancient Egyptian form of writing, *and* in Greek. This vital clue made possible the quick ability to decipher and understand ancient Egyptian symbols, for the two languages on the Rosetta Stone bore the same message. Hope for such a key was high at Knossos. The beginnings of a suspicion that perhaps the Minoans used an archaic form of Greek had slowly taken root in the mind of Michael Ventris.

Lack of a key, however, did not stop scholars, men and women, in many countries, who tried to break the Minoan language. Their work, in one volume, would be better reading than a dozen first class detective stories. From Cincinnati, Ohio, to Brooklyn, New York, from London, England, to Helsinki, Finland, they worked away at the task.

Michael Ventris kept records of the many systems he tried. No values for Minoan symbols came from them; nothing he worked on proved satisfactory. Excitement mounted when, in 1939, Cincinnati Professor Blegen was excavating at Pylos, in Greece. This site is believed to have been the home of Nestor, owner of the famous cup described by Homer. Professor Blegen, of the University of Cincinnati, had wonderful good fortune. He unearthed a large Mycenaean building and in it found hundreds of clay tablets with Linear Script B. Though some of the tablets were broken, it was a vital discovery.

All this time, the scholars had been working on the assumption that Linear B was a development of Linear A, a refinement of the older style. In 1950, this belief was discarded. Professor Blegen gave a student colleague the task of preparing the tablets for publication. The more scholars with printed copies of the tablets, the more likely that one of them would get a brilliant idea. *The key was hiding in Professor Blegen's own department!*

Professor Blegen's young American assistant, Emmett L. Bennett, during his examinations of the tablets, made a startling discovery! Though the scripts looked the same, they were not! He believed that though the symbols looked similar in both Linear A and Linear B scripts, they had different values. His notion, after he found it, seemed obvious, yet it is one of those recurring peculiarities: there are times we can look so hard that we miss what we seek because it is so close. Mr. Bennett wasted little time in communicating his idea to Michael Ventris.

The simple truth, as Bennett found it, cleared the way for progress. His idea is based on something we all know and use daily but seldom think about. America and most European countries use the same alphabet. But the words and speech neither read nor sound the same. The Linear scripts, though similar, were not related. *They were two different languages!*

Michael Ventris and Emmett Bennett kept close contact and exchanged ideas and progress reports. In 1952, working again at Pylos, Professor Blegen, digging at the other side of the house he'd excavated, found another cache of tablets! Missing parts of broken tablets from the first discovery were found here, too. Now there was abundant material for the work.

Michael Ventris returned to an earlier idea of his; were the symbols possibly an archaic form of Greek, after all?

He experimented, checking frequency of occurrence of certain symbols. He might discover the grammatic construction in this way. He gave experimental phonetic values, based on archaic Greek, to some of the symbols. To his great surprise, he found they matched! *He actually began to read the tablets!*

Still, this might only be coincidence. A few tablets proved nothing. His experiments would have to cover a much larger number before it could safely be considered he had found the right road. Bit by bit, as more tablets were shown to agree with the system Ventris was using, it was found to be truly based—and the work goes on today. But years may pass before all the tablets are read and printed for others to study.

The tablets which bore pictographs as well as written symbols proved fairly simple to decipher. And one disappointing truth became obvious. They were, as Sir Arthur Evans had suspected, lists of stores and goods. One tablet bore a pictograph that appeared to be a chariot. The written symbols when interpreted by the Ventris method, described a red-painted vehicle and its fittings. The vehicle was horse drawn, and had a center pole made of fig wood. Another tablet stood up under the same method of interpretation. This one bore pictographs of vases and tripods as well as writing. The archaic Greek symbols for tripod, which Michael Ventris applied to this tablet, proved them correct in their approach to the problem.

The work goes on, but not with Michael Ventris. In

1956 a promising young life was snatched from our midst. Thirty-four-year-old Michael Ventris was dead, killed in an automobile accident.

In July, 1960, Knossos, the Minoan civilization, and Sir Arthur Evans were again headlines in the presses of the world. Controversy about the age, origins, existence and extinction of the Minoans raged once again.

Some of the theories of L.R. Palmer, professor of Comparative Philology at Oxford University, England, who had spent seven years studying the Minoan civilization, were published in the Weekly Review of the *London Observer, The New York Times,* and other papers.

Professor Palmer challenged some of Sir Arthur's dates, facts and theories. Supposedly, in February, 1960, a daily log had been "found tucked away in a cupboard" at the Ashmolean Museum, and this was the basis of the cries of "hoax" and "fraud." This daily record, kept by one of Sir Arthur's assistants at Crete, "had been hidden away." It contradicted, in detail, some of the locations, depths and positions of certain finds at Knossos as reported by Sir Arthur Evans.

Which was correct—Sir Arthur's detailed books, or the "mysterious" daily log?

One fact was soon established. There was no mystery about the log at all! Dr. Donald B. Harden, director of the London Museum, and keeper of the Ashmolean from 1945 to 1956, immediately announced that the existence of the logs had long been known to scholars, who had used them in their studies of the intricate problems of the Minoan civilization. And the logs were those kept by Duncan Mackenzie, who worked with Sir Arthur at Knossos from 1900.

A rough rule of thumb for archaeologists is that objects found close to the surface of an excavation must have been the last buried there. Objects beneath are usually thought older and were buried earlier.

If, as the daily logs indicated, certain objects were found higher on the site than Sir Arthur reports, then this fact supported Palmer's contention that Knossos lasted several hundred years longer than Sir Arthur thought. Supporting evidence for this theory was found in 1952. The clay tablets and artifacts discovered at Pylos on the Greek mainland, by the American archaeologist Professor Blegen, match those found at Knossos.

Professor Palmer, familiar with the work of Michael Ventris and others, disagreed sharply with Sir Arthur, who believed Minoans created their civilization and colonized the mainland, much as Britain colonized large parts of the world from a small island. Palmer suggested, because of the common Greek language and similarity of artifacts discovered at Pylos and Knossos, that mainland Greeks colonized Crete.

Among the tablets found at Pylos is an inventory of furniture inscribed in the Linear B script, the same as that used by the last Minoans. One of these tablets was believed to read, "Aigeus the Cretan brought it." Professor Palmer, after studying the writing habits of what he described as "a certain scribe," concluded that the tablet really means "of Cretan workmanship with goat's head handles."

Whatever the outcome of this disagreement, from such constant care and checking, provided it is motivated by desire for truth, and not sensationalism, a greater clarity will emerge for other scholars and students.

Did Sir Arthur perpetrate a "hoax"? It is highly unlikely, and Professor Palmer quickly repudiated any such idea.

Was Sir Arthur wrong in his reconstruction of Minoan history and probable development?

Forty years is a long time, and Sir Arthur Evans assembled masses of material to bring into shape and order. That errors may have occurred is understandable. Also, it is true that Sir Arthur's love of Knossos and the Minoans made him unqualifiedly enthusiastic. He may have overstepped fact when attempting to bring his theories into focus. His eagerness to have the world know the glory that had been Knossos excited him, and this may well have led him to state as fact some things which a more sobered view would have presented as theory.

No doubt, too, the romantic in his nature occasionally led to some minor conclusions not strictly in accord with the known facts. This is humanly understandable, in view of the immensity of his task. But it also points a lesson. Men, if truth is to be their guide and master, must be forever on guard against traits in their own character which might lead them away from truth.

What if Professor Palmer's theory is upheld, that mainland Greeks colonized Crete, and not the other way around as thought by Sir Arthur Evans?

For the specialist, the purist, it is a vital point. But, what matters really is that Sir Arthur Evans opened for us a part of the past hitherto unknown and unsuspected. The glorious page, written by the Minoans in the story of man, has been dusted and cleared for us to read.

The piecing together of the story of Minoan civilization, each day, adds more substance to the "ninety cities" of Homer's *Odyssey*. Minos himself remains a shadowy figure.

The pursuit of the science of archaeology produces a patient breed of men. As Schliemann inspired Evans, and Evans inspired Ventris, has Michael Ventris, in turn, at some time in his short life, inspired another schoolboy? Will some other boy, in some country, read of *his* work and be compelled to follow the footsteps of Michael Ventris?

The island of Crete is littered with traces of Greco-Roman establishments, as well as Minoan remains, long lost to the world. Could it be that the Minoans *did* use papyrus for their books and poems? Did some wise Minoan nobleman, knowing the horror of earthquakes, hide a cache of books and records for posterity? Will some future archaeologist one day stumble across such a cache, perhaps in a bronze container which would preserve them against the ravages of time? As the now famous Dead Sea Scrolls were carefully hidden away, and accidentally discovered by an errant goat herder, did some far-sighted Minoan hide for posterity what will prove to be our first glimpse of Minoan literature—to be discovered by some persistent archaeologist?

To unearth such treasures, to pierce man's cloudy past, to reach the long departed as one way of improving the distant yet-to-come—such dreams lead archaeologists, like Sir Arthur Evans, to combat hardships, master frustrations, brush aside ill-motivated criticisms, and pursue their course on the limitless road to knowledge.

Bibliography

The dialogue employed in this book is the author's invention.

A rich storehouse of information is to be found in *The Palace of Minos* (Macmillan Company, London, 1921–1936), by Sir Arthur Evans, Member of the Bavarian, Royal Danish, Swedish, and Serbian Academies. Member of the Göttingen Society of Sciences, Royal Academy of Sciences, Amsterdam. Member of the German, Austrian, and American Institutes. Archaeological Society of Athens, Correspondent de L'Institut de France, Extraordinary Professor of Prehistoric Archaeology, Oxford University etc.

The following books offer the reader additional information and reference to the story of the Minoan civilization.

Cottrell, Leonard, *The Bull of Minos* (Rinehart & Company, Inc., New York, 1958)

Evans, Joan, *Time and Chance* (Longmans, Green & Co., Ltd., London, 1943)

Payne, Robert, *The Gold of Troy* (Funk & Wagnalls Company, New York, 1958)

Renault, Mary, *The King Must Die* (Pantheon Books, Inc., New York, 1958)

Vaughan, Professor Agnes Carr, *The House of the Double Axe* (Doubleday & Company, Inc., New York, 1959)

White, Anne Terry, *Lost Worlds* (Random House, Inc., New York, 1941)

Index

ABOUT THE AUTHOR

ALAN HONOUR is, in his own words, "American by choice, British by birth." He was born in London in 1918 and remained there to study until 1939, when he joined the Royal Air Force. Radio Intelligence assigned him first to Norway, later to the Middle East for four years, and then to France.

After the war, Mr. Honour returned to London. From there he went to France and to Italy, where he worked on film scripts. After that stint he traveled on to the United States, which is now his home. He lives in Richmond, Indiana.

In addition to SECRETS OF MINOS, he is the author of THE UNLIKELY HERO: *Heinrich Schliemann's Quest for Troy;* TEN MILES HIGH, TWO MILES DEEP: *The Adventures of the Piccards;* and CAVE OF RICHES: *The Story of the Dead Sea Scrolls.*